Mathematical Games

Mathematical Games

C. LUKÁCS

and

E. TARJÁN

TRANSLATED BY

JOHN DOBAI

Diagrams by J. Varga and E. Takáts

Illustrations by L. Réber and S. Gerö

BARNES & NOBLE

BOOKS

NEW YORK

This edition published by Barnes & Noble, Inc.
by arrangement with Souvenir Press.

1996 Barnes & Noble Books

ISBN 0-76070-095-8

Printed and bound in the United States of America.
M 9 8 7 6 5 4 3
FG

CONTENTS

1 **Games and Problems with Numbers** 7

Who Can Reach 100 First? Think of a Number. A Series of Weights. Guess the Number. Four Sevens. The Circled Number. Squares Within Squares. The Broken Board.

2 **Number Systems** 25

Guess the Number: Variation. Two Sides of a Coin. Chinese Signs. Multiplication at the Market.

3 **The Mysterious Nine** 34

The Telephone-number Game.

4 **Card Tricks** 39

Always the Fourteenth. Using "Magic Words." How the Mathematician Shuffled the Cards. The Secret Rules. Square of Cards. Counting with Cards. Four Aces. Nine Cards.

5 **Matches, Coins, Dice, and Dominoes** 54

Six Lambs. Matchgeometry. Sixteen Lambs. The Nimo Game. The Left Hand as a Computer. The Tak-Tix Game. Six Pennies. Turn the Dice. Guess the Throws. A Game of Chance. Guess the Domino. Who Is the Loser?

6 **Games for One** 72

The Cross Game with Six Pieces. The Cross Game with Nine Pieces. The Real Game of Solitaire.

7 **Games for Two** 84

Game with Cigars. Game of Square. She Loves Me, She Loves Me Not. Ticktacktoe. Battleships.

8 **Problems Through the Ages** 90

Some French Problems. Some Greek Problems. Ancient Arabian Riddle. An Old Hindu Riddle.

9 **Games with Geometry** 97

Changing a Rectangle into a Square. Changing a Square into a Rectangle. Changing a Rectangle into Another with Given Sides. Changing a Square into a Rectangle with a Ratio Greater Than One to Four. A New Linoleum. Cutting Up and Making a Loss. Another Chessboard. Different and Yet the Same. Knot the Handkerchief. Freeing the Index Finger. Inside or Outside? The Giant's Garters. String Bracelets. Magical Knots. Tricks with a Vest. Tricks with Rubber Bands.

10 **Writing in Code** 119

A Grid Code. Numbers Instead of Letters. Signs Instead of Letters. Rearranged Letters. Letters Instead of Numbers.

11 **Magical Squares** 133

Fill in the Squares. Move the Disks.

12 **Shapes and Sizes** 138

The Möbius Strip. Cut the Pencil. The Game of Squares. A String Game. Paper Folding.

13 **Mazes** 156

14 **Where Is the Mistake?** 160

The Clever Buyer. A Silly Argument. The Counterfeit Note. A Deceptive Triangle. Have We Lost a Square Inch? A Rope Around the Earth. A Bet. Rolling Coins. Deceptive Circles.

15 **Mixed Problems** 170

A Little Engineering. Fly Around the World. Six Barrels. An Odd Cork. A Number Game for Two or More. The Merchant as Mathematician. The Spider and the Fly. The Fly and the Honey. Will the Spider Catch the Fly? The Balance. A Dairy Problem. Clever Pipework. The Keen Chessplayers. Colored String. The Colored Regular Tetrahedron. Jack and Jill. Another Problem About Age. Good Luck! Squares from a Square. Husband and Wife. Who Is Guilty? The Three Friends. The Smith Family. The Round Table. Six Ladies.

CHAPTER 1

GAMES AND PROBLEMS WITH NUMBERS

Who Can Reach 100 First?

This game is easy to understand, and many people can be taken in by it. The game may be played several times without the opponent guessing the trick of winning.

Two players are needed. The winner is the one who reaches 100 first.

The person who starts – let's call him George – chooses a number. His partner – say, Ken – adds any number between 1 and 10. Now it's George's turn. The two players take turns in adding a number between 1 and 10 to the previous total.

Who will win? Who will get to 100 first?

The winner is the one who can make his opponent reach 99. If Ken reaches 89, then he has already won, because the largest number George can reach is 99. In order that Ken can reach 89 first, he must also reach 78 first. If we continue along these lines, Ken must also reach 67, 56, 45, 34, 23, and 12 first. If George does not know the game and he starts with any number other than 1, then Ken replies with a number which gives a total of 12. Already the winner has been decided, because George can increase this total by 10 at the most, giving a total of 22. Ken makes it 23, and so on, until the total of 100 is reached.

Different rules can also be used. It is possible to fix a target figure different from 100; the upper and lower limits for the numbers to be added can also be changed. We can win all the games if the sum of the largest and smallest number is subtracted from the target figure. In this way we get a series of numbers that ensures victory. If, for instance, the target is 80 and the numbers added must lie between 2 and 7, then the winning series will be $80 - 9 = 71$, $71 - 9 = 62$, then 53, 44, 35, 26, 17, and 8.

The same game has an even more exciting variation. Count out 40 matches. The two players take turns, removing at least 2 and not more than 5 at a time. The player removing the last match is the winner.

This problem is easy to solve: the winner is the one who leaves 7 on the table. Since his opponent must remove at least 2 and not more than 5, in the first case 5 and in the second 2 would be left. So that 7 matches will be left, the winner must also leave 14 previously. Similarly, this applies when the number left on the table is 21, 28, and 35. These are multiples of $5 + 2 = 7$. Therefore, if the person who starts knows the game, he simply removes 5 matches and the game is as good as won.

If, however, the person who knows the game does not start, he may not be able to win. Suppose that Ken knows the game, but George insists on starting. George takes 4 matches, leaving 36. In this case Ken cannot reach 35. It is possible that George will play into Ken's hands on the next move, but if George thinks about it logically, then whatever Ken's second move is, George can prevent Ken reaching 28. Therefore, Ken has lost the game.

If the rules are changed so that the loser removes the last two matches, the one who starts must try to leave two matches after his last move. This he can achieve if the number left after his next-to-last move is $2 + 2 + 5 = 9$. We get this number by adding, to the last number to be left, the smallest and the largest number that can be taken away. The number 9 can be reached if the previous total is $9 + 7 = 16$. Then, the previous totals are 23, 30, and 37. The person who starts must, therefore, remove 3 matches. Naturally, only the one who starts can be certain of winning.

Think of a Number

This is a well-known game with many variations. Let's have a closer look at some of the more interesting ones.

Katie says to Valerie, "Take a piece of paper and a pencil, think of a number, and write it down. Multiply it by 10 and take away the number you first thought of. Add 36 and cross out one of the figures in the final number (except the last one, if it is 0). Tell me the figures that make up the final number, in any order, and I will tell you the figure you crossed out."

Valerie writes down 312. She multiplies it by 10: 3,120. 3,120 − 312 = 2,808. 2,808 + 36 = 2,844. She crosses out the 8 and rearranges the remaining numbers: 4, 2, 4.

Katie adds these together, 4 + 2 + 4 = 10. She subtracts the sum from the nearest number larger than 10 that is divisible by 9, that is, 18. The remainder is the number Valerie crossed out.

Why does this work?

Valerie, when she had finished the sum set, arrived at a number divisible by 9. If any number is multiplied by 10 and the original is subtracted, then the remainder is 9 times the original number. If we add to this 36, that is, 4 × 9, then the sum will also be divisible by 9. We know that if the figures of a number divisible by 9 are added together, the sum will also be divisible by 9. So the missing figure, with the sum of the other figures, gives a number divisible by 9.

Valerie did not want to be outdone and asked Katie to think of a number. Then she said, "Double it, add 4, divide by 2, add 7, multiply by 8, subtract 12, divide the remainder by 4, subtract 11, and tell me the result. I'll tell you the number you thought of."

Katie thought of 11. 11 × 2 = 22, 22 + 4 = 26, half of 26 = 13, 13 + 7 = 20, 20 × 8 = 160, 160 − 12 = 148, 148 ÷ 4 = 37, 37 − 11 = 26. Katie tells Valerie the result: 26.

Valerie subtracts 4 (22), halves that, and says, "The number you thought of was 11."

Naturally, Katie is very curious. Valerie explains, "You take four from the final result, halve that, and you have the original number."

They try it several times, with different numbers, and the answer is always right.

Katie, not satisfied with merely knowing how it's done, also wants to understand each step.

She thinks of the problem as a basket containing so many eggs:

Multiply by 2:

Add 4; in this case, 4 eggs:

Halve the result:

Add 7:

Multiply by 8: 8 baskets and 72 eggs:

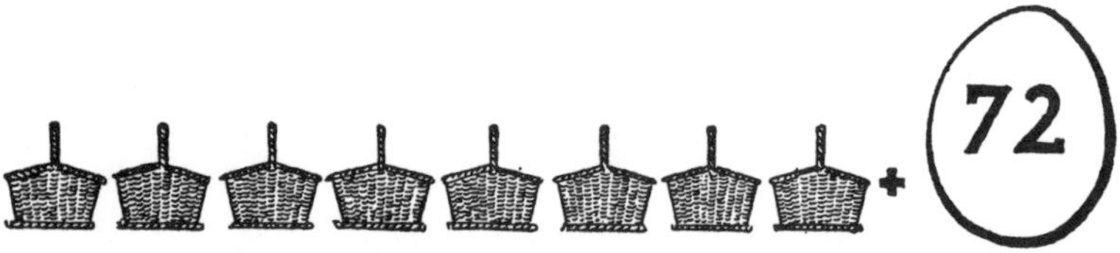

Subtract 12: 8 baskets and 60 eggs:

Divide by 4:

Subtract 11:

The result is 4 greater than twice the number thought of. So the other player takes away 4 and divides the result by 2 to arrive at the original number.

We can write the same thing in simple mathematical symbols. Let's call the number thought of x. We multiplied this by 2, giving $2x$. We added 4: $2x + 4$. We divided this by 2, giving $x + 2$. Added 7: $x + 9$. Multiplied by 8, giving $8x + 72$. Subtracted 12: $8x + 60$. This we divided by 4, giving $2x + 15$. Subtracted 11: $2x + 4$. Finally we arrived at twice the first number, plus 4. If, therefore, we take 4 from the final result and halve that number, we get the number first thought of.

Katie and Valerie decided to show these two tricks to Eva, who immediately wanted to show them a trick of her own. She began the same way: "Think of a number. . . ." Katie and Valerie together chose 7 as the number. Eva continued, "Multiply the number you thought of by 5 (35), add 2 (37), multiply the result by 4 (148), add 3 (151), multiply by 5 (755), finally add 7 (762), and tell me the result." Eva ignored the last two figures and said, "The number you thought of is 7."

Where's the trick?

Eva explains: "I don't know the number you thought of, so I called it x. Then I thought it out like this. You multiplied by 5 and added 2: $5x + 2$; multiplied this by 4: $20x + 8$; added 3: $20x + 11$; multiplied by 5: $100x + 55$; and added 7. This is a three-figure number in which the hundreds represent the figure x, the number you thought of. Therefore, if I ignore the last two figures, the remainder will give me the number you thought of."

Katie and Valerie found this trick in an old math book. They at once tried it out on their friend Kevin. The girls said, "We'll guess

your date of birth. Take the day of the month you were born, multiply by 20, add 3, and multiply the result by 5. Add to that the number of the month in which you were born, multiply by 20, add 3, multiply by 5, and finally, add the number formed by the last two figures of the year in which you were born. Then tell us the number."

Kevin was born on May 9, 1946. Therefore, the calculation went like this: 9; 180; 183; 915; 920; 18,400; 18,403; 92,015; 92,061. He told them the result. The girls subtracted 1,515, which left 90,546. The last two numbers give the year in which Kevin was born (after 1900), that is, 46; the number before those is the month, 5 (May); and the first number is the day, 9.

Let's have a look at how we found the unknown date of birth:

First we added	3
Multiplied by 5	15
Multiplied by 20	300
Again we added 3	303
Five times that	1,515

The number 1,515 has no connection with the date of birth; therefore, it can be safely subtracted.

Let's have a look at what's left. The day of the month was multiplied by 20, then 5, again by 20, and 5 again; that is, by 10,000. The number of the month was multiplied by 20, then by 5; that is, by 100. Therefore the result includes the number of the month times 100. The year of birth can be simply read off from the end of the final result; the number of hundreds gives the month and the number of ten thousands the day of birth. All this can be written down as mathematical symbols. Let's call the day a, the number of the month b, and the year c. Then the calculation goes like this:

The day of the month is multiplied by 20: $20a$. We add 3: $20a + 3$; multiply by 5: $5(20a + 3) = 100a + 15$. We add the number of the month, b: $100a + 15 + b$. We then multiply this by 20, giving $20(100a + 15 + b) = 2000a + 300 + 20b$.

We now add 3, which gives $2000a + 303 + 20b$. Five times this is $5(2000a + 303 + 20b) = 10{,}000a + 1515 + 100b$. We add the two figures from the year, that is, c: $10{,}000a + 1515 + 100b + c$. We write this down again in order: $10{,}000a + 100b + c + 1515$.

Therefore, if we subtract 1,515 we shall get a five- or six-figure number in which the first one or two figures (a) are the day, the next two the month (b), and the last two (c) the year of birth.

A Series of Weights

Most elementary balances have half-, one-, two-, five-, and ten-gram weights. However, we would like to discuss a rather peculiar series of weights. In this series there are only weights which can be expressed in terms of powers of three. There is a one-gram weight, since $3^0 = 1$. There is only one weight of each type. The problem is how to weigh any object that weighs less than 1 kg. (1 kg. = 1,000 grams). The following weights are available to us:

1 gram
3 grams
9 "
27 "
81 "
243 "
729 "

We are not obliged to use every weight each time. The heaviest weight we can weigh is by putting all the weights into one pan. This would give us 1,093 grams, whereas we will want to weigh only up to 1,000 grams.

This sort of problem is approached on a trial-and-error basis, even by a mathematician. Let us start: $1 = 1$, $2 = 3 - 1$, that is, we put the 1-gram weight in the same pan as the object we are weighing. $3 = 3$; $4 = 3 + 1$. 5 will be a bit more difficult, as the sum of the weights under 9 is 4. However, $5 = 9 - 3 - 1$. Then it becomes easier again: $6 = 9 - 3$; $7 = 9 + 1 - 3$; $8 = 9 - 1$; $9 = 9$; $10 = 9 + 1$; $11 = 9 + 3 - 1$; $12 = 9 + 3$; $13 = 9 + 3 + 1$. 14 – we are stopped once again, but remembering the previous occasion, we use the 27-gram weight; and we subtract from that: $14 = 27 - 9 - 3 - 1$. We can already see that we have a bit of difficulty when we have put all the smaller weights into one pan, the object to be weighed into the other pan, and the object is still a bit heavier. This was the case with 5 (one more than $4 = 3 + 1$) and with 14 (one more than $13 = 9 + 3 + 1$). We can forecast that the number after $1 + 3 + 9 + 27 = 40$, that is, 41, will be a bit difficult. Never mind! Let us use the 81-gram weight and we shall subtract from that. But perhaps we shall have not enough weights to subtract, since the gap between 41 and 81 is quite large. We must subtract 40 grams; have we sufficient weights? Yes, because the sum of all the weights below 81 grams is 40. Similarly, when we have difficulty with the number after $1 + 3 + 9 + 27 + 81 = 121$ (that is, 122), we shall use the 243-gram weight, and by subtracting 121 grams, all will be well. Consequently, we shall have trouble with the number coming after $1 + 3 + 9 + 27 + 81 + 243 = 364$ (that is, 365), since $729 - 365 = 364$. Is it completely by chance that we have managed so far? No, with all weights under 1 kg. we will be able to manage.

For example, if we want to weigh out 150 grams of sugar, we could try adding the weights together: $1 + 3 + 9 + 27 + 81 = 121$; that would be too little. Taking the 243-gram weight, we must subtract 93 grams from it, and we need $81 + 9 + 3$.

Or, if we need to weigh 617 grams, by adding we get $1 + 3 + 9 + 27 + 81 + 243 = 364$, which is too little. Taking the 729-gram weight, we must subtract $729 - 617 = 112$. First we subtract 81, leaving 31, which is $27 + 3 + 1$. Therefore, $617 = 729 - 81 - 27 - 3 - 1$.

Now we can confidently say that with these weights we can weigh any weight between 1 and 1,000 grams.

For the sake of the next trick, we shall write down the first forty numbers, using the sums and differences of powers of three.

$1 = 1$	$11 = 9 + 3 - 1$
$2 = 3 - 1$	$12 = 9 + 3$
$3 = 3$	$13 = 9 + 3 + 1$
$4 = 3 + 1$	$14 = 27 - 9 - 3 - 1$
$5 = 9 - 3 - 1$	$15 = 27 - 9 - 3$
$6 = 9 - 3$	$16 = 27 - 9 - 3 + 1$
$7 = 9 - 3 + 1$	$17 = 27 - 9 - 1$
$8 = 9 - 1$	$18 = 27 - 9$
$9 = 9$	$19 = 27 - 9 + 1$
$10 = 9 + 1$	$20 = 27 - 9 + 3 - 1$
$21 = 27 - 9 + 3$	$31 = 27 + 3 + 1$
$22 = 27 - 9 + 3 + 1$	$32 = 27 + 9 - 3 - 1$
$23 = 27 - 3 - 1$	$33 = 27 + 9 - 3$
$24 = 27 - 3$	$34 = 27 + 9 - 3 + 1$
$25 = 27 - 3 + 1$	$35 = 27 + 9 - 1$
$26 = 27 - 1$	$36 = 27 + 9$
$27 = 27$	$37 = 27 + 9 + 1$
$28 = 27 + 1$	$38 = 27 + 9 + 3 - 1$
$29 = 27 + 3 - 1$	$39 = 27 + 9 + 3$
$30 = 27 + 3$	$40 = 27 + 9 + 3 + 1$

Guess the Number

From what we have just learned it follows that all numbers can be expressed using the powers of three.

Using these, a "magic" table can be set up, with the help of which we can "guess" a number chosen by another person. The number should not be too big, say, less than 40. The first column of this "magic" table should contain all the numbers which when expanded, using the powers of three, will contain the term $+1$. These include 1, 4, 7, 10, 13, etc.

The second column should contain all the expansions where -1 occurs, e.g., 2, 5, 8, 11, 14, etc.

The third column should contain all the expansions where +3 occurs, and the fourth where −3 occurs.

The fifth column should contain, using the powers of three, all numbers where the expansion includes +9, and the sixth where the term −9 occurs.

The seventh column should contain all the numbers the expansion of which includes the term +27. Since we have set an upper limit of 40, there is no need to consider numbers where −27 occurs.

$1 + 3 + 9 + 27 = 40$, which is the largest number that can be made from these numbers.

If, therefore, someone thinks of a number and tells us in which column it occurs, by adding or subtracting the numbers at the top of the columns we can "guess" the number thought of.

I	II	III	IV	V	VI	VII
(1)	(−1)	(3)	(−3)	(9)	(−9)	(27)
1	2	2	5	5	14	14
4	5	3	6	6	15	15
7	8	4	7	7	16	16
10	11	11	14	8	17	17
13	14	12	15	9	18	18
16	17	13	16	10	19	19
19	20	20	23	11	20	20
22	23	21	24	12	21	21
25	26	22	25	13	22	22
28	29	29	32	32		23
31	32	30	33	33		24
34	35	31	34	34		25
37	38	38		35		26
40		39		36		27
		40		37		28
				38		29
				39		30
				40		31
						32
						33
						34
						35
						36
						37
						38
						39
						40

Let us imagine that someone thinks of 37. This occurs in columns I, V, and VII. Therefore, 1, 9, and 27 head those columns, all to be added; therefore, the number must be 37.

Again, if someone says that the number thought of occurs in columns II, IV, and VII, the solution is equally simple: $-1 - 3 + 27 = 23$.

If you are showing this to a number of people, then leave out the numbers in brackets; remember them in your head. This is quite easy to do.

Four Sevens

One of the teachers, Mr Cottrell, was careful to include little extras to make his lessons more interesting. One day he wrote this on the board:

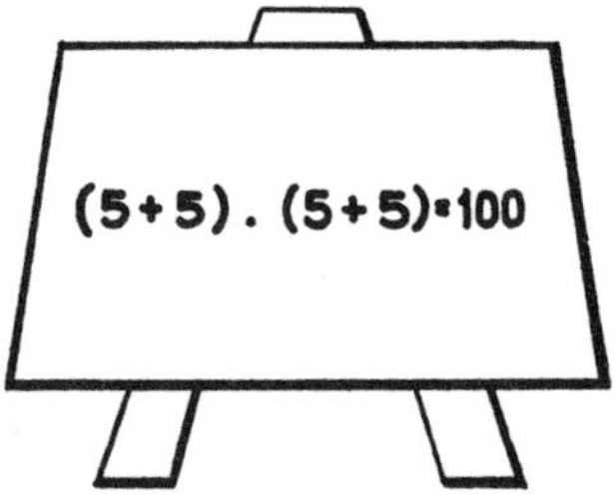

The four fives, being part of a simple sum, gave one hundred exactly.

"Now, who can do the same with four sevens?" asked the teacher. "Who can arrange four sevens in such a way that the result is exactly one hundred?"

George put up his hand. "I haven't managed it with four sevens, but can I use four nines like this: $99 + \frac{9}{9} = 100$."

"You are right," said the teacher. "Now I'll tell you how to use sevens. The way we have to write them down is a bit unusual, amounting almost to cheating."

Susan now put her hand up. "Sir, can we write down decimals over a whole number, thereby crossing out both?"

"You are on the right track! Write down your answer on the board."

She wrote: $\frac{7}{0{\cdot}7} \times \frac{7}{0{\cdot}7} = 100$.

"Quite right. Everyone can check it: $7 \div \frac{7}{10} = 10$, therefore giving $10 \times 10 = 100$."

"But, sir, this is true not only for sevens, but for all numbers."

"You are quite right. I am glad you noticed it."

$\frac{n}{0{\cdot}n} \times \frac{n}{0{\cdot}n} = 100$, whatever number n is, with the exception of zero. There is no point in dividing by zero.

The Circled Number

Here is a problem connected with the number 12.

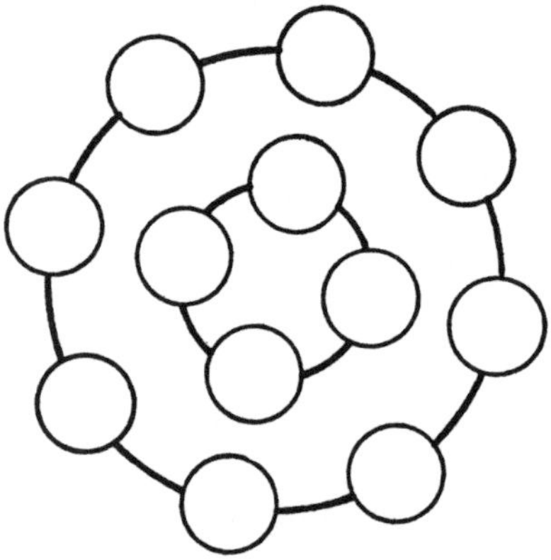

Write the numbers 1–12 in the circles in the diagram (using each number once only). The sum of the numbers in the outer circle must be twice the sum of those in the inner one. If you attempt this on a trial-and-error basis, you will not have an easy task, as there are 30 possible answers.

How do we get so many?

If we add together the numbers between 1 and 12 we get 78. This must be divided so that there will be twice the number in the outer circle (52) as there are in the inner one (26).

The numbers between 1 and 12 can be arranged in thirty different groups of four, each group adding up to 26.

1, 2, 11, 12	2, 3, 9, 12	3, 4, 9, 10
1, 3, 10, 12	2, 3, 10, 11	3, 5, 6, 12
1, 4, 9, 12	2, 4, 9, 11	3, 5, 7, 11
1, 4, 10, 11	2, 5, 8, 11	3, 5, 8, 10
1, 5, 8, 12	2, 5, 9, 10	3, 6, 7, 10
1, 5, 9, 11	2, 6, 7, 11	4, 5, 6, 11
1, 6, 7, 12	2, 6, 8, 10	4, 5, 7, 10
1, 6, 8, 11	2, 7, 8, 9	4, 5, 8, 9
1, 6, 9, 10	3, 4, 7, 12	4, 6, 7, 9
1, 7, 8, 10	3, 4, 8, 11	5, 6, 7, 8

If we make the problem more difficult, by saying that the inner circle must contain consecutive numbers only, then there is only one solution: 5, 6, 7, 8.

The following two problems are a bit more difficult, but they can be solved if you know a little algebra.

Squares Within Squares

This is similar to the previous problem. The task is to write such numbers in the diagram that the sum of the squares of two adjacent

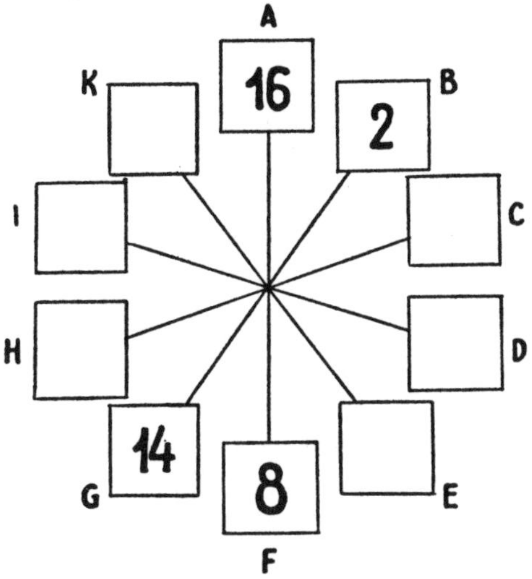

numbers is the same as the sum of the squares of the two on the opposite side of the diagram. For example, put 16 in square A and 2 in square B. $16^2 = 256$; $2^2 = 4$; $256 + 4 = 260$. We said that $F^2 + G^2$ must be the same. Suitable numbers would be 8 and 14, because $8^2 = 64$; $14^2 = 196$; $64 + 196 = 260$.

Similarly $B^2 + C^2$ must be equal to $G^2 + H^2$; also, $A^2 + K^2 = F^2 + E^2$.

What numbers must we write in the empty squares? Only whole numbers may be used. Since $A^2 + B^2 = F^2 + G^2$, then $A^2 - F^2 = G^2 - B^2$; in other words, the difference between the squares of numbers on the same diagonal must always be the same. In our case, the difference is $16^2 - 8^2 = 14^2 - 2^2 = 192$

Similarly, $C^2 - H^2 = 192$.

But the difference between the squares of two numbers must be equal to the sum of those numbers multiplied by their difference. Using symbols: $(x - y)(x + y) = x^2 - y^2$.

Therefore, we can write: $(C + H)(C - H) = 192$.

The result 192 also tells us that $(C + H)$ and $(C - H)$ cannot both be odd numbers; otherwise, their product would not be even. If one (say, $C + H$) is even, then the other must be as well, because the sum of the difference of the two numbers can be even only if both numbers, C and H, are even or if both are odd.

Expand 192, using even numbers: 2×96, 4×48, 6×32, 8×24, 12×16.

Therefore:

$$\begin{array}{r} E + K = 96 \\ E - K = 2 \\ \hline 2E = 98 \\ E = 49 \\ 2K = 94 \\ K = 47 \end{array}$$

And these numbers then can be written instead of C and H.

Further:

$$\begin{array}{r} C + H = 48 \\ C - H = 4 \\ \hline 2C = 52 \\ C = 26 \\ 2H = 44 \\ H = 22 \end{array}$$

When we insert the numbers into their positions, it seems as if it does not matter which we take as I and which as H. However, we must take care. If in one pair the larger number is in the upper half of the diagram, we must be sure that the larger number is in the pair next to it in the lower half, since the sum of the squares of two larger numbers cannot give the same result as the sum of two smaller ones. Continuing in this fashion, we can get the other numbers too (see diagram).

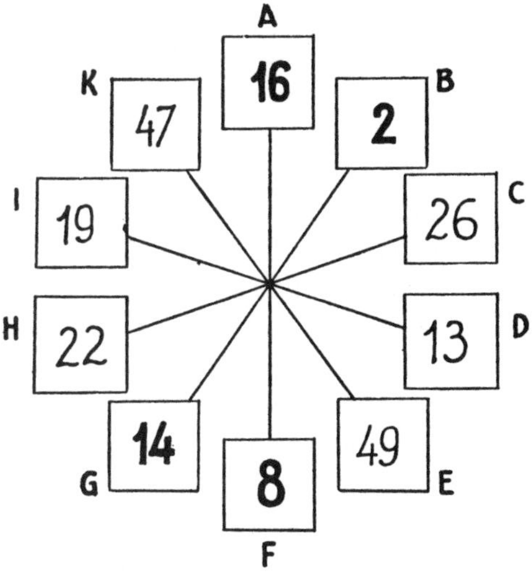

The Broken Board

Susan was very interested in how numbers are related to each other. As soon as she saw a number, her imagination started working until she found something interesting about it.

"Look, Claire," she said to her friend. "Look what I have noticed. Can you see that broken board?"

Claire said, "Yes, I can see it. What about it? It says 3,025."

"See how two numbers were left when the board was broken, 30 and 25. If we add them together, we get 55. And 55 × 55 (that is, 55^2) is 3,025, which is the original number," said Susan proudly.

"Yes, you are right," said Claire. "Let's find other numbers which are similar, and then we can tell the teacher about it at the next math lesson."

So they took pencils and paper and tried out various numbers.

Suddenly Claire exclaimed, "Eureka! 9,801." Indeed, 98 + 1 = 99, and 99 × 99 = 9,801.

A few days later at school Susan wrote down the numbers in question on the board.

"What do you think?" asked the teacher. "Are there any other four-figure numbers of this type?"

"Please," said George, "is there a way of finding such numbers without using a trial-and-error method?"

"Yes," said the teacher. "George is thinking about this just as a mathematician does when he keeps trying to find a general rule to cover all possible solutions. Let's have a look at 2,025: 20 + 25 = 45 and 45 × 45 = 2,025."

"But our numbers are better," shouted Claire.

"What do you mean by better?"

"Well, in our numbers all the digits are different."

"You are right," said the teacher. "But 2,025 cannot be excluded for that reason; let's see how many numbers of this type there are."

They tried and tried, but apart from 3,025 (55 × 55), 9,801 (99 × 99), and 2,025 (45 × 45), they could not find any others. The teacher then explained that there are none.

Why?

The four-figure number must be given by the square of a two-figure number; let's call this a^2. Let us call the two two-digit numbers x and y. We are saying that the two-figure numbers are added, that the result is squared, and that we get back to the original four-figure number. That is: $(x + y)^2 = a^2$; or $x + y = a$; and $y = a - x$.

As we can see from Claire's example, we can think of 01 as a two-figure number, and even 0000 is a satisfactory four-figure number.

On the other hand, in the original four-figure number, x can be regarded as the number of hundreds (expressing the thousands as hundreds) and y the units (expressing the tens as units). Consequently, a^2 (the original number) can be written as: $100x + y = a^2$.

We know that y equals $a - x$; therefore, substituting:

$$100x + a - x = a^2$$
$$99x = a^2 - a$$
$$99x = a(a - 1)$$
$$x = \frac{a(a - 1)}{99}$$

As we said at the beginning, x must be a whole number. This can only happen if $a(a - 1)$ can be divided by 99 without a remainder being left (99 can be expressed as 9×11). x can be a whole number in four cases:

1. $a = 99$ when the fraction is simplified so we get $x = 98$ and $y = 1$, giving the four-figure number as 9,801.

2. $a - 1 = 99$. But then $a = 100$, which we cannot use, as $a^2 = 10{,}000$, which is a five-figure number.

3. a is divisible by 9, and $(a - 1)$ by 11. How do we find a number like that?

Let us write down the one- and two-digit numbers which are divisible by nine and the numbers which are one less than these:

a	$a-1$
9	8
18	17
27	26
36	35
45	44
54	53
63	62
72	71
81	80
90	89
99	98

The only pair of numbers which satisfies all our requirements is 45 and 44. In this case, when we simplify our equation, we get: $x = 20$ and $y = 25$, giving 2,025 as the four-figure number.

4. a is divisible by 11 and, $(a - 1)$ by 9.

Draw a table. In this case write in the column headed a the two-figure numbers which are divisible by 11.

a	$a-1$
11	10
22	21
33	32
44	43
[55]	[54]
66	65
77	76
88	87
99	98

Then $a = 55$ and $a - 1 = 54$, from which we get $x = 30$, $y = 25$, and the four-figure number 3,025.

From this it is obvious that there can be only three numbers which can be made to work in this way: 9,801, 2,025, and 3,025.

CHAPTER 2

NUMBER SYSTEMS

We all know the Roman numerals. We can imagine how difficult it must have been for the Romans to do even simple arithmetic.

Imagine that you have to add MDCLIV and CDLXXXVIII. If you try adding them by writing them down one over the other in the normal way, you will get into a fine pickle. The difficulties you would face if you tried multiplication and division are too terrifying even to be contemplated.

Why is the decimal system so much easier to use? There are two reasons. The first is that the 0 was invented, and the second is that the value of a digit depends on its position within a number. The Roman V means five whether it occurs in XV or in VII. But in our system the figure 5 stands for different values in, for instance, 35 and 53; in the former it means 5 and the latter 50. In other words, when the position of a number changes, so does its value. When the Romans wrote MDC they meant M + D + C. If in algebra we write the expression *abc* we mean $a \times b \times c$. When we write 753, this means neither $7 + 5 + 3$ nor $7 \times 5 \times 3$. We all know that what is meant is $7 \times 100 + 5 \times 10 + 3$, or $7 \times 10^2 + 5 \times 10 + 3 \times 1$. In other words, each number is multiplied by a power of 10, and the products are added together. (The number of units, in this case 3, is multiplied by $10^0 = 1$.)

Every number can be regarded as being made up of different multiples of various powers of 10. The numbers show how many times a power of 10 has to be multiplied. Since 10 is the base number, we call this system the decimal system of counting. The powers of 10 are:

$$10 = 10^1$$
$$100 = 10 \times 10 = 10^2$$
$$1{,}000 = 10 \times 10 \times 10 = 10^3$$
$$10{,}000 = 10 \times 10 \times 10 \times 10 = 10^4$$
$$100{,}000 = 10 \times 10 \times 10 \times 10 \times 10 = 10^5$$
$$1{,}000{,}000 = 10 \times 10 \times 10 \times 10 \times 10 \times 10 = 10^6$$

and so on.

This system was probably begun because people started counting by using their fingers, of which they have 10.

But we do not use the decimal system always in everyday life; for instance, in measuring time, angles, lengths, and weights.

There is no reason why, instead of using the powers of 10 for counting, we should not use the powers of another base number.

If we use the powers of 2 we get a binary system of numbers. The powers of 2 are $2^0 = 1$, $2^1 = 2$, $2^2 = 4$, $2^3 = 8$, $2^4 = 16$ and so on.

Let's have a look at how numbers appear in the binary system. The digits 0 and 1 keep their original value.

$2 = 1 \cdot 2^1 + 0 \cdot 1$. If we use the same system of abbreviation that we used with the decimal system and do not write down the powers of two, merely the number these powers are to be multiplied by, the number two will be written as 10. Here are a few more numbers using the binary system:

$$
\begin{aligned}
3 &= 1 \times 2^1 + 1 \times 1 = 11 \\
4 &= 1 \times 2^2 + 0 \times 2^1 + 0 \times 1 = 100 \\
5 &= 1 \times 2^2 + 0 \times 2^1 + 1 \times 1 = 101 \\
6 &= 1 \times 2^2 + 1 \times 2^1 + 0 \times 1 = 110 \\
7 &= 1 \times 2^2 + 1 \times 2^1 + 1 \times 1 = 111 \\
8 &= 1 \times 2^3 + 0 \times 2^2 + 0 \times 2^1 + 0 \times 1 = 1{,}000 \\
9 &= 1 \times 2^3 + 0 \times 2^2 + 0 \times 2^1 + 0 \times 1 = 1{,}001 \\
10 &= 1 \times 2^3 + 0 \times 2^2 + 1 \times 2^1 + 0 \times 1 = 1{,}010
\end{aligned}
$$

We do not use the binary system in everyday life, as we need rather a lot of digits to write down even a small number. As you saw, 10 is written as 1,010, and a larger number needs even more, (e.g., 73 is written as 100,101). In scientific and technical subjects, however, the binary system is used more frequently.

One of the most interesting modern inventions is the computer. These machines can do arithmetic at tremendous speed. For instance, they can do 70 multiplications in a second where the numbers to be multiplied all contain 10 digits. These machines work so fast and so accurately because they do not depend on mechanical devices – such as gear wheels. They depend, as radio and television sets do, on electronic valves or transistors. These computers use a system in which all numbers can be expressed by using only two digits. So you can see what an important place binary numbers occupy in modern technology.

However, binary numbers can be used to solve less serious problems. Many amusing games and tricks can be played using them.

Guess the Number: Variation

Take a piece of paper and write down the five columns of numbers shown here. The table appears to be arranged without order.

1	2	4	8	16
3	3	5	9	17
5	6	6	10	18
7	7	7	11	19
9	10	12	12	20
11	11	13	13	21
13	14	14	14	22
15	15	15	15	23
17	18	20	24	24
19	19	21	25	25
21	22	22	26	26
23	23	23	27	27
25	26	28	28	28
27	27	29	29	29
29	30	30	30	30
31	31	31	31	31

Ken asks George to think of a number between 1 and 31 and say which columns contain the number he thought of. George tells Ken that the number he thought of appears in columns 1 and 5. Ken answers at once that the number thought of is 17. George would like to know how Ken got the answer and examines the table closely. Finally he puzzles out how it is constructed.

In the first horizontal row, the powers of 2 appear (1, 2, 4, 8, 16); this is easy to discover. But the second row is more difficult to work out. George soon discovers the following rules: The table contains all the numbers between 1 and 31. All the numbers can be written as sums of the powers of 2. For example, $23 = 16 + 4 + 2 + 1 = 2^4 + 2^2 + 2^1 + 2^0$, or $15 = 8 + 4 + 2 + 1 = 2^3 + 2^2 + 2^1 + 2^0$, or $18 = 16 + 2 = 2^4 + 2^1$. The first column contains all the numbers which, if expanded in this way, contain 1. The second column contains the numbers whose expansion includes 2, the third column the numbers which include 4, the fourth 8, and the fifth 16. George had thought of 17, which can be expressed as $16 + 1$ and, therefore, appears in the first and fifth columns. So we can guess the number thought of by adding the numbers which appear at the top of the said columns.

This game can be even more surprising if we write down the columns on separate strips of paper. We again ask someone to think of a number between 1 and 31 and to tell us on which strips the number appears. These strips we then hand over, keeping only those on which the number does not appear. We add the numbers at the head of those columns and subtract the sum from 31. If, for example, the number thought of is 25, which occurs in columns 1, 4, and 5, we hand these over. We are left with the second and third columns. We add the numbers at the top and subtract from 31. $2 + 4 = 6$, $31 - 6 = 25$.

Two Sides of a Coin

Ken goes out of the room, and Mary asks George to think of a number between 1 and 31. George thinks of a number and tells Mary, who then lays a few coins on the table. Ken is called in, looks at the coins, and guesses the number at once.

George is getting used to thinking in binary numbers by now, and after a few trials he discovers the trick. He remembers that there are only two digits used, 0 and 1. The coins have two sides, heads and tails, so Ken and Mary must have agreed that heads represents 0 and tails 1. Since $13 = 1 \times 2^3 + 1 \times 2^2 + 0 \times 2^1 + 1 \times 2^0$, Mary used four coins and put them out as: tails, tails, heads, tails.

It's more difficult to discover how this trick is done if the two partners use coins of different values or if they do not place them in a straight line. Of course, those who do not know the binary system will never discover the answer.

Chinese Signs

There is an interesting story connected with binary numbers. In a Chinese manuscript dated 3000 B.C., sixty-four different signs were found, each sign consisting of six parallel horizontal lines, one above the other. Some of the lines were continuous and others were broken:

Scientists spent a long time wondering what these signs represented. Finally Leibnitz, the German philosopher and mathematician, gave a possible solution. According to his theory, the signs represent the first 64 numbers, written in binary form. The digit 0 is represented by a broken line and 1 by a continuous line. Regarding the lines in each sign from the bottom to the top we get:

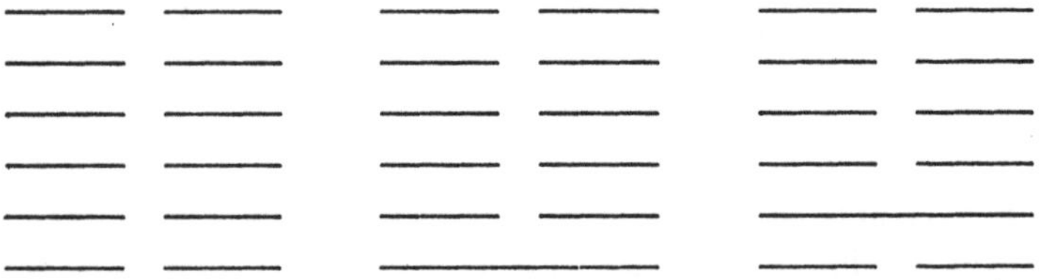

0 1 2

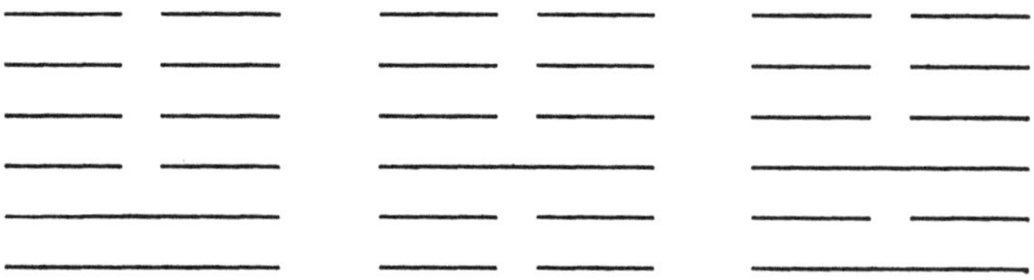

3 4 5

The last two are:

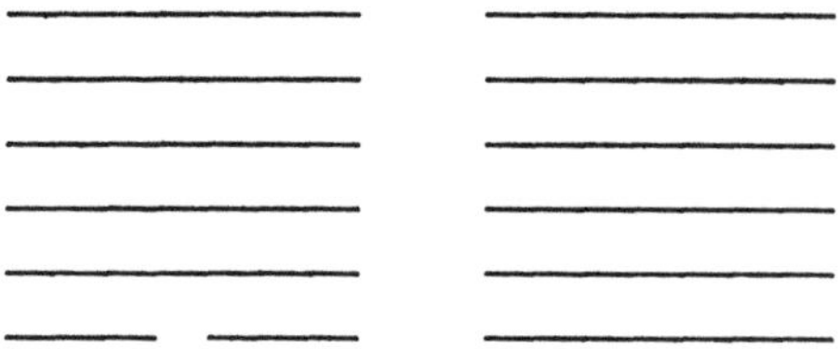

62 63

Multiplication at the Market

The other day I went to the market to buy apples. I bought three pounds at $11\frac{1}{2}$ pennies a pound. The old lady calculated how much I owed her like this:

$$\begin{array}{r} 11\frac{1}{2} \\ 11\frac{1}{2} \\ 11\frac{1}{2} \\ \hline 34\frac{1}{2} \end{array}$$

It's a good thing I was not buying 37 pounds, or she would have had to write $11\frac{1}{2}$ down 37 times.

Then I thought, perhaps she would be grateful if I taught her a way of multiplying which needed only multiplication by 2, division by 2, and adding. Here it is! Let us multiply 27 by 38. Write down the two numbers at the head of two columns. Multiply one column by 2 and divide the other by 2. If we get an odd number, let us disregard the remainder, which, of course, is 1. Continue multiplying and dividing till the result in the right-hand column is 1. We get:

~~27~~	38
54	19
108	9
~~216~~	4
~~432~~	2
864	1
1,026	

We cross out the numbers in the left-hand column which are opposite even numbers in the right-hand column; then, adding the remaining numbers in the left-hand column, we get the result: $27 \times 38 = 1{,}026$.

Let us try another, slightly longer example: 47×89.

47	89
~~94~~	44
~~188~~	22
376	11
752	5
~~1504~~	2
3008	1
4,183	

$$47 \times 89 = 4{,}183$$

At first glance the whole thing appears to be very mysterious, but it becomes less so if we start using the binary system. Let us write down 38 in the binary system: $38 = 32 + 4 + 2 = 1 \times 2^5 + 0 \times 2^4 + 0 \times 2^3 + 1 \times 2^2 + 1 \times 2 + 0$. 38 written in the binary system is 100110.

Therefore:

First column	*Second column*
$27 = 27$	$38 \div 2 = 19$ remainder 0
$2 \times 27 = 54$	$19 \div 2 = 9$,, 1
$2^2 \times 27 = 108$	$9 \div 2 = 4$,, 1
$2^3 \times 27 = 216$	$4 \div 2 = 2$,, 0
$2^4 \times 27 = 432$	$2 \div 2 = 1$,, 0
$2^5 \times 27 = 864$	$1 \div 2 = 0$,, 1

Reading the remainders in column two, from the bottom to the top, we get 38 expressed in the binary notation: 100110.

Where in the second column the remainder is 0, there is a 0 in the binary system; part way through the multiplication, multiplying by 0 cannot occur; therefore, we cross out the numbers opposite these in the first column. In our example, we multiplied by 27, that is, $2^5 + 2^2 + 2$, which is exactly 38.

CHAPTER 3

THE MYSTERIOUS NINE

The class was learning about the division of whole numbers. Everyone knew that numbers can be divided by nine if the sum of their digits can also be divided by nine.

Miss Brown, the teacher, suddenly noticed that Angela was eagerly putting up her hand.

"What is it, Angela? Is there something you don't understand?"

"No, Miss Brown. I only wanted to say that a lot of people think that the number nine is a magic number. Is it true?"

"Well, Angela, no number has magic properties, but it is no coincidence that people say that there is magic in the number nine. It has a number of, not mysterious, but interesting properties."

"Tell us about them, please, Miss Brown," said the class.

"All right," she said, "we shall devote today's lesson to this. Let's take a number. For example: 718,639,573. Adding up the digits gives us 49. We can see that our number cannot be divided by nine, since the sum of its digits is indivisible by 9. If we add the digits of 49, we get a two-digit number, 13. If we divide both this and the original number by 9, we shall have 4 as the remainder in each case.

"The remainder after dividing by nine can be most useful for checking the results of additions or multiplications. If we divide each number in an addition sum by nine, and add the remainders, we will get the same figure as the remainder when we divide the total of the addition by nine. Using this in multiplication, we divide the individual numbers to be multiplied by nine; and the remainders when multiplied by each other give the same total as the remainder we obtain after dividing the final result by nine.

"For example:

579	remainder after dividing by nine	= 3	sum 18
314	" " " "	= 8	remainder (÷9)
+853	" " " "	= 7	= 9
1,746	" " " "	= 9	

"When multiplying:

3,572 × 43	the remainders after dividing by nine	= 8 × 7 = 56
14,288	" " " "	= 2
10,716	" " " "	= 7
153,596	" " " "	= 2

" Can we now say that if we have tested a calculation by dividing by nine, it is sure to be correct? Unfortunately not. We could have made a mistake that would give the correct result when divided by nine, and yet it would still be incorrect. Here is an example of this sort of mistake if two digits are changed around: 579 + 314 + 853 = 1,764. Although when we divide by nine it seems that all is well, the calculation is incorrect. Such a mistake is very easily made when copying a calculation from once piece of paper onto another. That is why it is best, when working on a calculation, to do the arithmetic on the same page as the rest.

"So we see that if the test with the nine does not work, the calculation is definitely incorrect; but if it does work, it doesn't necessarily mean that it is correct, as the above example shows.

"What we have been saying is equally true with numbers other than nine. Yet we prefer to stick to the number nine. Why is this? Because the remainder will be the same as the sum of the digits, as each ten, hundred, and thousand gives 1 as a remainder.

"If the original number is divisible by nine, then the remainder after dividing by nine is zero. Quite a few tricks are based on numbers which can be divided by nine. Here are two examples:

"1. Write down any number. Mix up the digits and subtract the smaller from the larger.

"Cross out one digit of the result and tell me what you are left with. I will guess what number you crossed out, with one stipulation. You must not cross out a zero."

Someone wrote down the number 85,271 and mixed it up as 15,728.

$$\begin{array}{r} 85{,}271 \\ -15{,}728 \\ \hline 69{,}543 \end{array}$$

The 5 was crossed out, and the others were read out: 6, 4, 9, 3. Back came the answer that the number omitted was 5.

"2. Write down a number and add up its digits. Subtract this from the first number. Cross out one digit of the result and tell me, in any order, the other digits, and I will guess the number you crossed out."

$$\begin{array}{r} 381{,}075 \text{ (sum of the digits} = 24) \\ -\quad 24 \\ \hline 381{,}051 \end{array}$$

The 1 was crossed out, leaving 1, 8, 3, 0, 5. Again, back came the answer, "You crossed out the 1.

"Now, do you think this was done by magic? Can anyone explain this?"

Finally Angela came up with an answer. "I think that the sum of the digits of any number does not depend on their order. If, therefore, the digits are all mixed, then the remainder after dividing by nine will be the same after mixing as before. If two such numbers are subtracted from each other, and the remainder after dividing the difference by nine is zero, then the difference is divisible by nine. If we cross out one digit of the difference and we add the remaining digits (the order of them, naturally, does not matter), then the number we crossed out must be such that it gives a number divisible by nine with the other digits. That is how we get zero as the remainder.

"In an example just now, the difference was 69,543. This is divisible by nine. The 5 was crossed out; the other digits were added together $6 + 4 + 9 + 2 = 22$. The nearest number which can be divided by nine is 27, and 5 must be added to 22 to get 27."

"Very good," said the teacher.

"I haven't quite finished, yet," said Angela. "In the second example, we subtracted the sum of the digits from the number. This number has the same remainder as the original number. In other words, it's the same as the first example."

The teacher praised Angela's logic; then she said, "You've forgotten only one thing. Why did we say that zero should not be crossed out?"

At least ten hands went up.

"Now, George, you tell us."

"If zero is crossed out, then the sum of the digits is left unchanged; therefore, it is uncertain whether zero or nine was crossed out."

"Good! I can see that these problems interest you. Now, I shall write a four-figure number on the board. You will give me another four-figure number, which I'll write underneath. It's my turn with the third, and so on. I shall write down the total of these on a piece of paper before we start, and afterward we can check if I was right."

The teacher wrote	3,845
the children	1,528
the teacher	8,471
the children	2,911
the teacher	7,088
	23,843

They had a look at the piece of paper, and the number on it was the same.

Several children volunteered to give an answer to this one. They quickly noticed that on adding individual digits of the second and third rows, the total of each was nine. It was the same with rows four and five. The sum of the second and third rows is 9,999; so is the sum of the fourth and fifth rows. The sum of the last four rows is 2 less than 20,000; the total therefore is 20,000 plus the first row minus 2.

The Telephone-number Game

Write down an imaginary telephone number; for example 354276. Mix up the figures so that we get a new number, e.g., 573642. Subtract the smaller number from the larger. The result is 219366. Add the figures together, and we get 27. Add the digits of 27 together, and the result is 9.

If we start at the star on the funny dial shown in this drawing and make the same number of steps clockwise as the result of a calculation such as the one above, we shall always end up at the spiral figure. Why is this so, when we can start with any number?

The remainder nine merely depends on the sum of the figures; therefore, it does not change if we mix up the digits. If we subtract two numbers whose remainder is the same, then the result will be divisible by nine, and, therefore, the sum of the digits can also be divided by nine.

Our peculiar dial has nine symbols on it, so that starting with the first, we shall always reach the last with nine steps.

CHAPTER 4

CARD TRICKS

Always the Fourteenth

Let's take 27 cards out of a pack. Ask someone to take a card, to note which it is, and to replace it in the pack. With a little shuffling and manipulation, we can easily work out which card it was.

Lay out three rows, each containing nine cards face-up. Ask which row contains the card that was taken out. Gather the three rows together so that the row containing this card is in the middle of the pack. Again divide the pack into three rows of nine and ask which row contains the chosen card. Pick up the rows again, as before. Repeat this a third time.

Finally, count out 14 cards, the fourteenth being the card picked.

Now we shall explain how this is done.

Let us imagine that the cards are numbered from 1 to 27 in the order in which they are first laid out. Then the cards would look like this:

1	2	3
4	5	6
7	8	9

10	11	12
13	14	15
16	17	18
19	20	21
22	23	24
25	26	27

Suppose that number 19 is the card picked. Then we could pick up, for example, the row that starts with 2, then the row with 1, and then the row headed by 3. When we lay these out again they will look like this:

2	5	8
11	14	17
20	23	26
1	4	7
10	13	16
19	22	25
3	6	9
12	15	18
21	24	27

The chosen card is in the first column again; in this case, therefore, we pick up the cards so that the column which begins with 2 is in the middle, by first picking up the column starting with 5 and finally the column headed by 8.

The third time we lay them out we will get this:

5	14	23
4	13	22
6	15	24
2	11	20
1	10	**19**
3	12	21
8	17	26
7	16	25
9	18	27

This time number 19 is in column 3, so we shall put that row in the middle.

If we were to lay them out a fourth time we would get:

5	4	6
2	1	3
8	7	9
23	22	24
20	**19**	21
26	25	27
14	13	15
11	10	12
17	16	18

Number 19 is the fourteenth card, that is to say, it is exactly at the center of the pack, having 13 cards before and 13 cards after it.

So, as we showed you, it is not necessary to lay them out the fourth time, but merely to count out the fourteen cards.

Using "Magic Words"

Take ten pairs of cards and ask someone to choose a pair and to note which pair was chosen. Then lay out the twenty cards in four rows, each containing five cards. This is not done just haphazardly, but with the help of the "magic words." Look at these four Latin words: *mutus*, *dedit*, *nomen*, *cocis*. These words together have no particular meaning but have interesting properties. Each word consists of five letters. In every word there is only one letter that occurs twice. In the first, it is *u*, *d* in the second, *n* in the third, and *c* in the fourth. Also, any two words have one letter in common. In the first and second word the letter in common is *t*, in the first and third *m*, in the first and fourth *s*, in the second and third *e*, in the second and fourth *i*, and in the third and the fourth *o*.

If we lay out the cards so that each pair replaces a letter which is common between two words and then ask the person to point out the row or rows containing the chosen pair, we can pick out the right pair whether they point to one row or two.

Let us picture the above four words:

1. *mutus*
2. *dedit*
3. *nomen*
4. *cocis*

If, for example, the chosen pair are in the first and fourth rows, then the cards represent the letter *s*.

Naturally, the order of the words can be changed so that people will have even greater difficulty in guessing how it was done; but if you decide to do this, you must take care to remember the changed order of the "magic words."

This game can be developed further by laying out three of a kind instead of pairs. For eight such groups we have thought of four "magic words." Here they are: *lanata*, *levete*, *livini*, *novoto*.

There are $4 \times 6 = 24$ letters representing $3 \times 8 = 24$ cards. In each word there are three letters the same, and in any three words out of the four you will find that there is only one letter in common. If, then, the group of three cards are in lines 1, 3, and 4, then they must represent the letter *n*.

How the Mathematician Shuffled the Cards

As soon as they see something new, most mathematicians want to formulate a scientific law around it. The Frenchman Monge (1746–1818) was no exception, and he did some research on the shuffling of cards. He was interested in finding a way of shuffling which would give the dealer the power to decide in advance which cards each player will receive.

Related to this is a simple card trick sometimes known as the Monge trick.

The trick consists of someone drawing one card out of a pack, then, after noting it, putting it back, saying only how many cards are there above it.

The "conjurer," after shuffling, "guesses" which was the card in question.

The trick does not depend on a sleight of hand. The person doing the trick has no chance of seeing the card, and the success of the trick depends on the way the cards are shuffled.

The pack is placed face-down on the table, and the first card is picked up. The second card is put on top of the first, the third being put under the first, the fourth again on top, and the fifth on the bottom. We continue shuffling the cards until the chosen card gets back to its original place. Then the other cards will be back in their original places as well, and we merely count out the cards until we reach the card with the given number.

Two questions arise: Do we always get back to the original order, and how many times must we repeat the shuffling to do so?

To the first question the answer is easy. We always get back to the original order, since there are a finite number of ways that a number of cards can be arranged, although the shuffling may have to be repeated many times.

The answer to the second question is not so simple. It is obvious that the number of shuffles required depends on the number of cards we start with.

Let's have a look at the number of shuffles required if we start with eight cards.

Original order	1, 2, 3, 4, 5, 6, 7, 8.
After the first shuffle	8, 6, 4, 2, 1, 3, 5, 7.
After the second shuffle	7, 3, 2, 6, 8, 4, 1, 5.
After the third shuffle	5, 4, 6, 3, 7, 2, 8, 1.
After the fourth shuffle	1, 2, 3, 4, 5, 6, 7, 8.

Therefore, starting with eight cards, four shuffles are necessary to get back to the original order.

If someone draws a card and puts it back in the pack so that there are five cards above it, we shuffle the cards four times and count out six cards after the fourth shuffle.

What happens if we are playing with an odd number, say, nine cards? The ninth card will always be placed at the bottom of the pile, and so its place will be unchanged. So the number of shuffles will be the same as if we were dealing with only eight cards. Therefore, if we want to find the number of shuffles, we must consider only the even numbers.

Monge drew up a table showing the connection between the number of cards and the number of shuffles necessary.

Number of cards	*Number of shuffles*
2	2
4	3
6	6
8	4
10	6
12	10
14	14
16	5
18	18
20	10
32	6

The Secret Rules

The following card game differs from the generally known games by an important feature: it has no fixed rules. For every hand, the players must discover the rule in the course of the playing.

The game is played by at least three people with a deck of 52 playing cards. One person is the leader and at the same time the dealer. The leader determines the rule of the game, but he does not tell the other players; instead he writes it on a slip of paper so that it can be verified later on. Then he deals the cards, not giving himself any, so that the other players each receive the same number of cards. One card must be left over; this will be the lead-off card. Thus 51 cards are to be divided among the players. This of course is possible only if 51 is evenly divisible by the number of players. Otherwise, a number of cards must be set aside that will permit the remaining cards to be evenly distributed among the players. For example:

Players	Cards to be set aside	One player receives
2	1	25
3	0	17
4	3	16
5	1	10

Suppose that the leader of the game invents the following rule: on a red card you always must place a black one, and on a black card you always must place a red one.

The play begins. The leader puts down the lead-off card. On this card the first player places one from his hand *without thinking*, since he has no way of knowing the rule. If by chance he happens to have played in accordance with the rule, the dealer says "correct," and this card remains on the lead-off card.

If not, the leader says "wrong," and the player must take back the card and place it on the table in front of him.

When all the cards have been put down, this hand is finished. Now the "good" cards are in the middle of the table and the "bad" ones are in front of the players. Naturally fewer cards will remain to the player who was the first to discover the rule of the game and knowingly put down the correct cards. But how is it possible to discover such a rule? This is not always such an easy thing to do; for example, if this is what the players see:

From this it is possible to draw several different conclusions:

1. On an even card an odd one must be placed, and on an odd card an even one must be placed.
2. On every card must be put a card either one higher or one lower in value.
3. On a red card must be put a black one, on a black one a red one.

When only a few cards have been put down, many kinds of hypotheses are possible. However, if someone now puts the queen of hearts on the 9 of spades, and the leader accepts this, then of the three foregoing suppositions only the last can be correct. The person who discovers this can now quickly dispose of his cards. After every completed hand, another player becomes the dealer.

After every hand, a list is made of the number of wrong points of each player, in other words, of how many cards remain in front of each player.

From this the scores of the dealer and the players are determined in such a way that the better the player, the higher the score.

First the dealer's score is decided. Suppose that besides the dealer there were three players, A, B, and C. A was left with 10 wrong cards, B with 5, and C with 3. Thus C was the best player, and twice the number of his remaining cards, or 6, will be subtracted from the total number of wrong cards of the two other players, or 15: $15 - 6 = 9$. This becomes the dealer's score. In other words, the dealer's score is obtained by multiplying the number of wrong cards of the best player by the number of other players, and subtracting the result from the combined number of wrong cards of the *other* players.

The players' scores are obtained in the following way: The number of wrong cards of a player is multiplied by the number of other players, and the result is subtracted from the total number of wrong cards of the other players. If the subtrahend (number to be subtracted) is larger than the minuend (number from which it is to be subtracted), the player's score becomes 0. If a player has no cards remaining, 6 bonus points are added to his calculated score. After the entire game is finished, the player who has gotten the most points is the winner.

In the example given, where A has 10 wrong cards left, B 5, and C 3, player A would have a score of $(5 + 3) - (2 \times 10)$, which is impossible, because 8 is smaller than 20; therefore A has a score of 0. B's score is $(10 + 3) - (2 \times 5) = 3$ points, and C's score is $(10 + 5) - (2 \times 3) = 9$ points.

If in addition to the dealer there are 4 players, A, B, C, and D, and the number of wrong cards per player is, respectively, 2, 3, 10, 1, then the scores become:

Dealer: $(2 + 3 + 10) - (3 \times 1) = 12$
A: $(3 + 10 + 1) - (3 \times 2) = 8$
B: $(2 + 10 + 1) - (3 \times 3) = 4$
C: $(2 + 3 + 1) - (3 \times 10) = -24$, i.e., 0
D: $(2 + 3 + 10) - (3 \times 1) = 12$.

After the scores are written down, the next hand begins.

Now let us look at a few cases where it is very difficult to figure out the rule from the order of cards put down:

Rule: the card put down must be either the same suit or the same value as the preceding card.

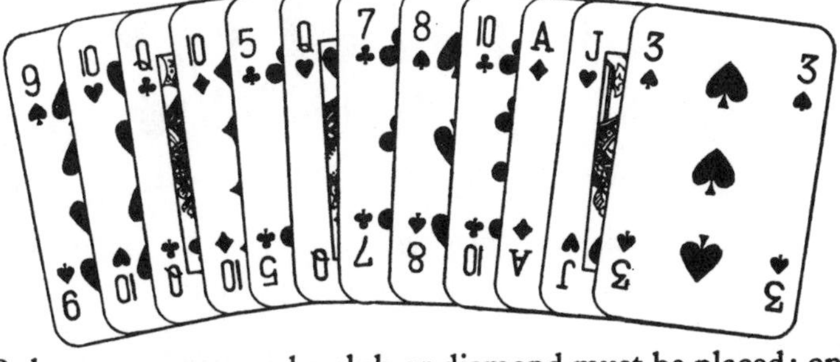

Rule: on an even card a club or diamond must be placed; on an odd card a heart or spade must be placed.

Rule: on the face cards, a red card must be put down; on the numbers, a black card must be put down.

Rule: if the value of the card divided by 3 leaves a remainder of 0, a diamond must be put on it; if the remainder is 1, a heart must be put on it; if the remainder is 2, a spade must be put down.

Rule: on a black card, two red cards must be placed, then 3 black cards, 4 red cards, 5 black cards, and so on.

In making up the rules for the game, distinctive personal characteristics of the individual players may even be used. For example:

if a player's name begins with a consonant, he must put down a red card; if his name begins with a vowel, a face card.

Since there is an enormous variety of possibilities to consider, discovering the rule becomes quite difficult.

Square of Cards

In the diagram we can see a square made up of all the cards between the ace (1) and ten of diamonds. Katie and Jamie made this, but they were not very happy with the "result." What they had wanted to do was to arrange the cards in such a way that the number of points in the top row, in the bottom row, and in the two sides (using the corner cards in both cases) added up to the same number.

In our diagram, the number of points in the top and bottom rows and the column on the left add up to 14, but in the column on the right they add up to 23.

The two children tried every way of making the cards add up to 14, but in vain. The question is: Can the cards be arranged so that all the four sides add up to 14 or some other number?

Katie's brother, Matthew, offered his help.

"It can be done," he said, "but you must not insist that the number they add up to should be 14."

"Why?" protested the children.

"Look at it this way. On the ten cards, the sum of all the points is 55. Right? Suppose that you have managed to arrange the cards so that the sum of the points in each side is 14, then there would be $4 \times 14 = 56$ points. But the points of the corner cards are used twice, and so $56 - 55 = 1$ would be the sum of the points of the four corner cards, and this is clearly impossible. Therefore you will never succeed in what you are trying to do!

"So what shall we do?" continued Matthew. "Let us try arranging the cards so that the points on each side add up to 18. I think we should be able to do this. $4 \times 18 = 72$. Subtracting 55, we get 17; therefore the points on the four corner cards should add up to 17. Let us try this: let the four corner cards be the 2, 6, 4, and 5; then, $2 + 6 + 4 + 5 = 17$. Using these, we can make a square so that the points on each side add up to 18.

"If we change the corner cards around, we shall get different answers, but since the basics remain the same, these cannot be regarded as totally different. We can arrange the middle cards differently as well, but these cannot be regarded as different, either. If, however, we make up 17 using numbers other than those above, for instance, $8 + 1 + 6 + 2$, then the arrangement will be:

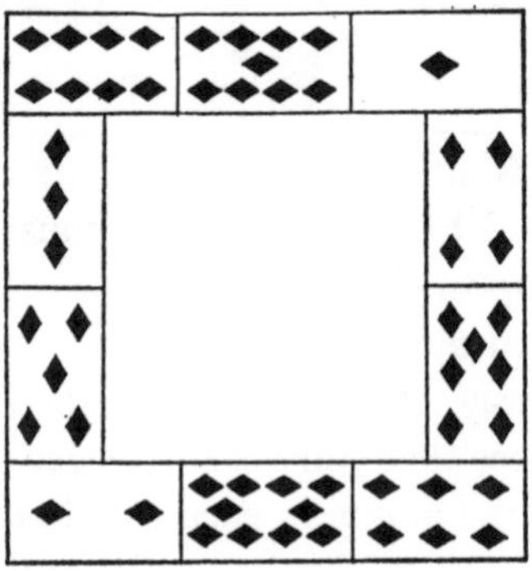

Naturally, 18 is not the only number that the points on each side can be added up to; and, in fact, squares can be arranged in which the points on each side add up to 19, 20, 21, and 22.

Counting with Cards

The number 142,857 is quite an interesting one. If we multiply this with any number between 1 and 7, the same numbers will occur in the result as in the number with which we started. Furthermore, their order will be as follows:

Let us write down the digits of the original number around the circumference of a circle. Whichever one we start from, we shall get the digits of the original number rearranged in a so-called cyclic way.

For example, if we multiply 142,857 by 3 we get 428,571, that is, we go around the circle starting from the 4.

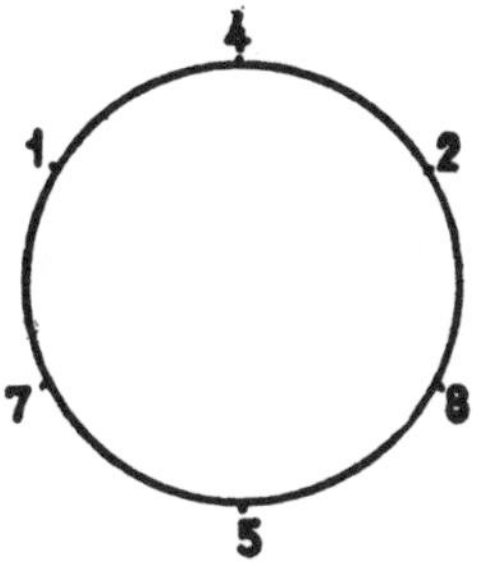

We can use this to show you a card trick. We take out the cards 1, 4, 2, 8, 5, and 7 from a pack of cards, and to our partner we give a set containing a 2, 3, 4, 5, and 6.

We spread out our cards on the table in the order 1, 4, 2, 8, 5, 7, and ask our partner to take one card from his hand and multiply 142,857 by the number on that card. While he is doing this (probably using paper and pencil), we can rearrange the cards, with one movement, to give the same result. If, for example, our partner says he is going to multiply by 4, we know that the last digit of the result must be an eight, because $4 \times 7 = 28$. Therefore we take the cards 5 and 7 from the end of our number and put them in front, to give 571,428, which is $4 \times 142,857$.

Four Aces

Robert took a pack of cards and asked someone to say a number between 10 and 20. The number was 15. Robert then counted out 15 cards from the pack, so that the card which was originally on top was now on the bottom and the fifteenth card was on the top. There were two piles of cards on the table. The digits of the number chosen were added together ($5 + 1 = 6$). Robert then took six cards from the top of the smaller pile and put them back on top of the larger. The seventh he placed, face down, to one side; then he replaced the rest of the smaller pile on top of the larger one.

He again asked for a number between 10 and 20, and he then repeated the previous operation till he had four cards turned face down to one side. Then he turned these four. They were the four aces.

The same trick using different numbers produced the same result.

We will let you in on a secret. There is a little bit of cheating here – the pack is arranged before the start so that the aces are numbers 9, 10, 11, and 12 from the top. If the sum of the two digits of a number which itself has two digits is subtracted from that number, the result will be a multiple of 9. When a second number is chosen, card number 10 will occupy position 9, and so on.

Nine Cards

John said to his friends, "I will select the following cards from a suit. Ace, two, three, four, etc., the nine being the last. Any of you can shuffle them and then put them on the table. Bill, Fred, Steve – each of you draw one card from the nine and note which it is, without telling me. Bill, you start; multiply the value of your card by 2, add 1, multiply by 5, and whisper the result to Fred.

"Fred," continued John, "you add the value of your card to the one whispered to you by Bill. Multiply the result by 2, add 1, multiply the result by 5, and whisper the result to Steve." Steve did the same, and when he finished, John asked him for the final figure: 3,805. "In that case," said John, "Bill drew the three, Fred the two, and Steve the five."

They tried the game several times, but the result was the same: John could always guess which cards they had drawn.

Finally, he explained the trick. "Bill drew one card from among the nine. Let's call its value x. He doubled it: $2x$; added 1: $2x + 1$; and multiplied by 5: $10x + 5$. In other words, Bill got a two-figure number ending in 5, with the number of tens the same as the number on the card that he drew.

"Now Fred adds his number: $10x + y + 5$; multiplied by 2: $20x + 2y + 10$; adds 1: $20x + 2y + 11$; multiplies by 5: $100x + 10y + 55$.

"Steve adds his number: $100x + 10y + z + 55$: then $200x + 20y + 2z + 110$; then $200x + 20y = 2z + 111$; finally $1000x + 100y + 10z + 555$.

"So I merely subtract 555 from the final figure, and the first figure of the remaining four-figure number is the value of the card drawn by Bill, the second that of the card drawn by Fred, and the tens give the value of the card drawn by Steve."

"What happens," asked Bill, "when not three, but two or four people draw cards?"

"There is no real difference," said John. "From the final figure a number is subtracted consisting of as many fives as there are players (that is, 55 if two play, 555 if three play, etc.)."

CHAPTER 5

MATCHES, COINS, DICE, AND DOMINOES

With a few simple things – a box of matches, several coins, a pair of dice, a set of dominoes – we can show our friends quite a few amusing and interesting tricks and games. We are not thinking of conjurer's tricks, only the sort when a little thought is of far more use than "magic."

Six Lambs

My little brother Peter wanted to put six toy lambs into a pen made of 13 matches, which formed six equal spaces. Like this:

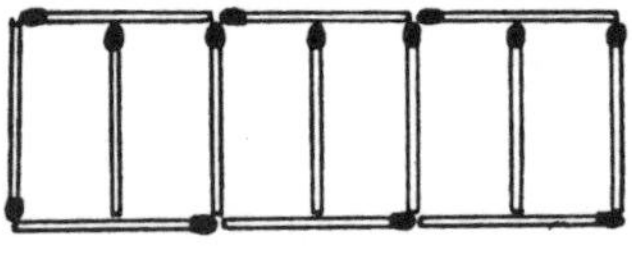

While he was doing this, he accidentally broke one of the matches. What will happen to the sixth lamb? It will surely wander out of its open pen and get lost!

I tried to help him find a way of making equal pens for six lambs out of the 12 remaining matches.

For those who cannot find a way, I will show them. Like this:

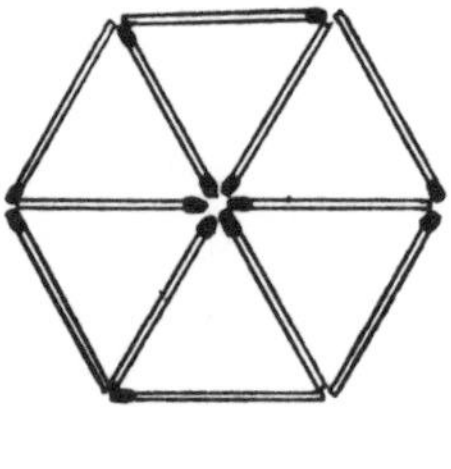

Matchgeometry

In the drawing you can see two rectangles made up of 18 matches.

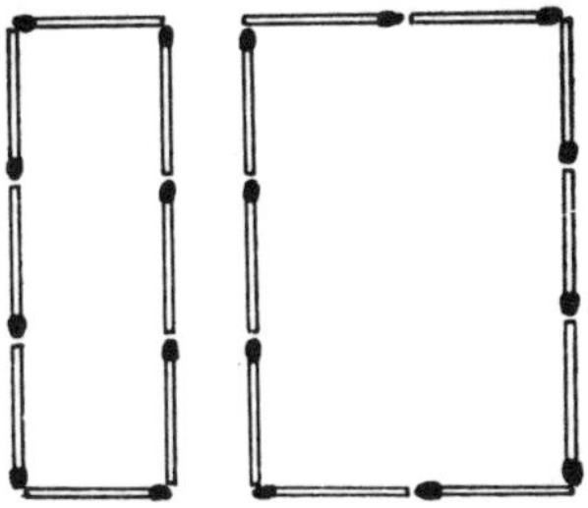

You can see at once that the area of the rectangle on the right is twice that of the one on the left. How can we rearrange the 18 matches so that we again have two rectangles, but the area of one is three times that of the other? And if we can do this, then let us try to make two pentagons so that the area of one is three times the area of the other. In both cases all the 18 matches must be used.

Let us have a look at the first problem.

Using 6 matches, make this rectangle:

The area of this is 2 units.

Now make the parallelogram shown below, where the base is 4 matches long and the height is exactly 1·5 matches long; therefore, its area is $4 \times 1{\cdot}5 = 6$ units, three times that of the other.

The second question is more difficult. One starts off by thinking about regular pentagons, and this does not work.

The broken lines within the smaller pentagon form five equilateral triangles, and fifteen in the larger one. Therefore, the area of the larger pentagon is three times that of the smaller.

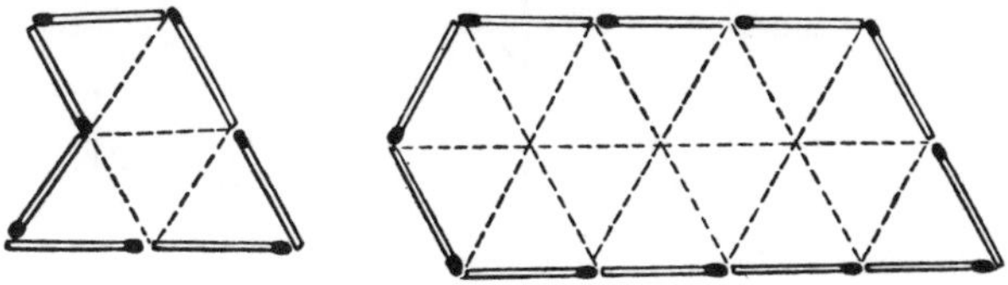

Sixteen Lambs

Make a square 4 × 4 using sixteen matches; this is the fold. We must make pens for the lambs (they are represented by the circles). Walls within the fold (9 matches) divide it into four parts holding 8, 3, 3, and 2 lambs each. The question is: How can we, by changing the position of two matches, change the number of pens to 3, each holding 6, 6, and 4 lambs?

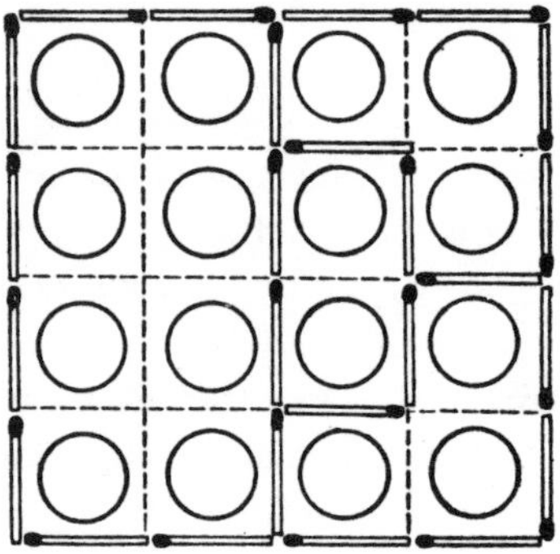

The outside walls must not be moved, and neither must the lambs; only 2 matches out of the 9 within the fold can be moved.

If we succeed in doing this, let us try the same thing, changing the position of 3, 4, 5, 6, and 7 matches in turn.

The diagrams below show the solutions; the thick lines show the matches whose positions were changed.

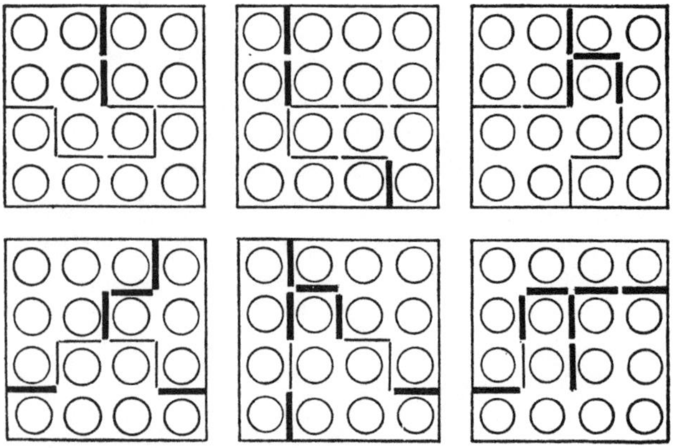

The Nimo Game

Mr Brown, who always had good ideas for games, told his sons Johnny and Andy, "I'll give you my box of matches, and I'll teach you an interesting game – the Nimo Game. The game is played like this. You can lay out three groups of matches, say, 3 in the first group, 4 in the second, and 5 in the third:

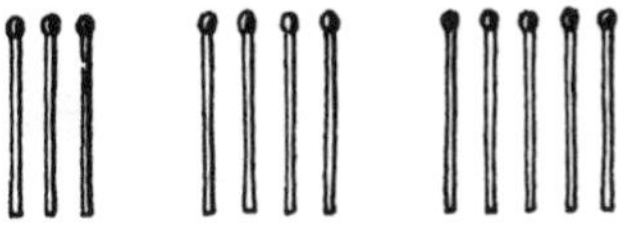

"The players, taking turns, remove as many matches as they wish from any one group. The winner is the one who takes the last match. Naturally, you can have more groups of matches, and the number in each group can be varied too."

The boys began to play. At first they played rather haphazardly, so that first one, then the other, was the winner; but then Andy suddenly exclaimed, "I've just noticed something! If, during the game, two groups contain the same number of matches, and it's your turn, then I've won, whatever you do."

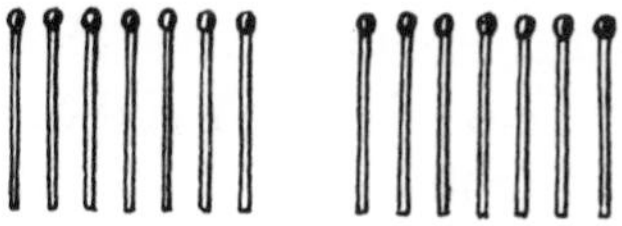

Johnny would not believe this, but Andy explained, "It's quite simple. If you remove a certain number from one group, then I remove the same number from the other group. When you have removed one group completely, I can take the other group, including, of course, the last match."

Johnny was amazed, and Mr Brown praised Andy. He told the boys that sometimes the Nimo Game was played so that the person who removed the last match was the loser. Andy decided to work out a certain way of always winning in this case, too. But whatever he tried, he could not succeed.

The large number of matches confused him.

"Let's try it with only a few matches. Assume that we have only two groups, each group with only two matches."

Johnny agreed, and now it was his turn.

He took one match from one group, and then Andy took both from the other, leaving Johnny with the last match.

"Let's try it again," said Johnny. "Maybe I can beat you."

Johnny removed the whole of one group and Andy took one match from the other, and the last was again left to Johnny.

Andy then became really excited. "This is interesting! When there are two groups, each containing the same number, then I can win even though the person who takes the last match is the loser. I simply wait till both groups contain 2 matches each, and then I play as I have just now."

But Johnny wouldn't leave it at that. "Suppose this situation does not occur; for example, your opponent leaves you with two groups, each containing only one match. Then you will have to take the last one."

"Yes, that's true," said Andy. He suddenly had an idea. "Imagine that all the groups but one contain only one match, and the remaining group has more than one. Then, if there is an even number of groups, I remove the whole of the group which contains more than one match, so that an odd number of groups remains, each containing one, and my opponent must remove the last one. If, however, there is an odd number of groups, I remove all but one from the group which contains the most, and we get back to the previous situation." They tried this, and it worked.

The boys realized that one could work out a system of winning, whether he had to leave or take the last match.

They asked Mr Brown to tell them all the winning situations. "All right, I'll tell you. You will win if in one group there is one match, in the second two matches, and in the third three matches. Try it!"

Mr Brown helped Johnny a little. They played that the winner had to take the last match.

Andy eagerly started and took one from the group containing three, and Johnny took away the single match, leaving the 2–2 situation, which they already knew was a winning one. From this, it was obvious that it would not have mattered if Andy had taken the single match, because then Johnny would have taken one from the group containing three matches, and again they would have been back to 2–2. Andy tried again – from the original 1–2–3 position – taking one from the group containing two; then, when Johnny took away the whole of the group containing three matches, they were left with 1–1, and it was Andy's turn. Again it was obvious that Johnny would win. Andy would not give up. He started afresh and took two away from the group of three matches, Johnny took the two matches from the second group, leaving 1–1, and Andy again had to acknowledge defeat. Finally Andy tried to take away all of the third group; when Johnny took one from the group containing two, again they were back to the 1–1 position.

Andy was a bit disappointed at losing all the time. "Let's try the 1–2–3 position again, but the one who takes the last one will be the loser."

Johnny started. They agreed it was not a good idea either to move the single match or to remove all of the group of three, because they would get to the 2–2 position. Johnny took one away from the group of two and Andy took two from the group of three, leaving 1–1–1. Johnny took one, Andy another, and Johnny had to take the last one, which meant that he lost.

So that they could be certain, they started again. Now Johnny took two from the group of three and Andy one from the group of two; the position was 1–1–1, signaling Johnny's defeat.

When they started again, Johnny took away the whole of the group of three. Andy took away both of the group of two, leaving the last match to Johnny. So in this way they had tried out all the possibilities.

They began to wonder who would win if both players knew the game, and how to be sure of winning. They soon discovered that the one who starts loses, because his opponent can counter every move he makes.

Mr Brown added, "If someone learned all the moves so that he didn't need to refer to a book, he could play the Nimo Game like a machine, in fact, without thinking. Since the rules of the game can be easily learned, some scientists built an 'electronic brain' to play the Nimo Game. This machine not only played the game well, but it also won. The first of these machines was exhibited in London in 1951, and later in Berlin and in several cities in the United States."

The Left Hand as a Computer

The two boys soon tried out the things they had learned. They kept showing the Nimo Game to their classmates, and it soon became obvious that their knowledge of the game was rather limited. They could win only if they were faced with two equal groups or a 1–2–3 position, but they did not know how to reach such a position. If we are playing with two or more groups containing different numbers of matches, we cannot rely on our opponent to play into our hands every time.

The class asked Mr Cottrell, their math teacher, to talk to them about it. This is how he explained it. "You already know a number of winning positions. These are 2–2, 3–3, 4–4, 5–5, 6–6, etc.; also, the 1–2–3 position. But apart from these, there are a number of other situations which guarantee success, provided we can recognize them. You would be surprised to know that binary numbers could help us, wouldn't you?"

They were all amazed to hear this. They already knew about binary numbers, but they were not expecting to see them popping up here. The teacher continued, "Suppose we have three groups of matches, one containing three, the second four, and the third five matches.

"Let's write these down as binary numbers:

3 can be written as	11
4 can be written as	100
5 can be written as	101
Total	212

"The two outside columns give two, and the middle column one. If all the digits in such a number are zero or even, then the situation is favorable for winning; but if any one of the numbers is odd, the position is not favorable. An unfavorable situation can be converted into a favorable one for winning. The only question is, how?

"If someone, for instance, sits down to play from a 3–4–5

position and wants to convert this to a position favorable for winning, he must convert the middle number in the above sum into a zero or a two. This figure represents two matches in the first group. Therefore, with his first move he must remove two matches from the group of three. Indeed, he can't do anything else or he will not change the sum of the middle column into an even number, but he may change the other numbers into odd ones."

The class was happy to find a system which was so easy to remember. They tried it, practiced it, and at the next session came up with a question: "With the small numbers we have been dealing with, it's easy to remember the binary equivalents. But with larger numbers we have to take paper and pencil, and this makes the 'trick' less effective. How can we make the conversion easy to remember?"

The teacher answered in this way. "If any one group contains not more than 31 matches, then we can use our left hand as a computer."

"Use our left hand as what?" asked the boys.

"Certainly! Suppose we start the game with four groups containing 7, 13, 24, and 30 matches. I am the player to start. Is this a favorable situation for winning? It can be decided in this way. I open the fingers of my left hand palm upward.

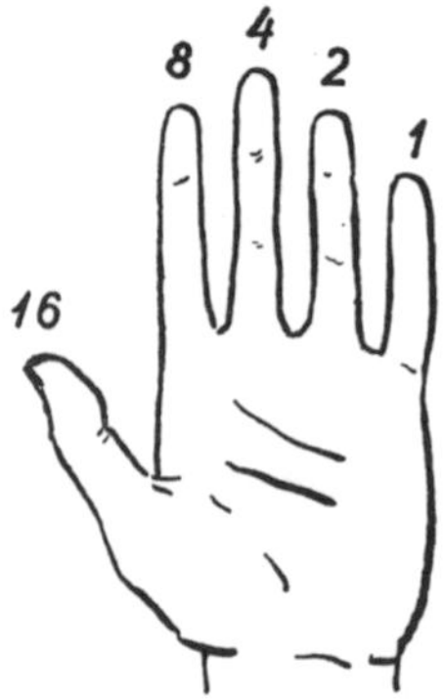

"The thumb represents 16, the index finger 8, the middle one 4, the third finger 2, and the little finger 1. The number of matches in the first group is 'fed' into my computer like this: $7 = 4 + 2 + 1$; I fold my third, fourth, and little fingers into my palm. Now, with the number $13 = 8 + 4 + 1$, I must fold my index finger and third finger; but this is already folded, as is the little finger. Therefore, I must straighten them. I similarly 'feed' in 24 and 30; $24 = 16 + 8$ and $30 = 16 + 8 + 4 + 2$.

"If, at the end of the whole operation, all my fingers are opened, then the situation is favorable. Why? Because my open fingers signal either zero or the even numbers 16, 8, 4, 2, and 1; and we need every power of two to be even or not to be there at all."

The whole class started to open and fold the fingers of their left hands. The quicker ones soon discovered that with the game starting with 7–13–24–30, the situation was not favorable because the index and third fingers remained folded.

One member of the class, Tom, said, "It doesn't matter, sir; if I am starting I can soon alter this with my first move. We saw that even if both players know the game, the one who starts loses. Therefore, with my first move I must remove the odd numbers of powers of two. Naturally, I can take matches from one group only."

"That's right, Tom. Have a look at how these numbers look in the binary system."

So Tom wrote down this table:

	16	8	4	2	1
7			1	1	1
13		1	1	0	1
24	1	1	0	0	0
30	1	1	1	1	0
	2	3	3	2	2

There were two odd numbers after the columns were added. How could they make both of them even with one move? Tom came up with the answer: "One correct move could be to take twelve from the group of 13, that is, to leave one match only. Another would be to take 4 from the group of 24, which could be regarded as taking away 8 and adding 4. Therefore, the number of eights would decrease and the number of fours would increase, changing the sums of those numbers into even ones. It would be even simpler to take 12 from the group of 30, looking at 12 as $8 + 4$."

"That's fine, Tom," said Mr Cottrell; "but before we leave all this, let's have a look to see why the situation is favorable when the sum of the columns of the binary numbers is even or zero. In other words, what is the connection between the Nimo Game and the binary system? I'll tell you straight away that we can win if the number of groups of matches is even, since then we can merely 'imitate' the move of our opponent. We can do this also if there are even numbers of 16, 8, 2, and 1. We can treat each power of two as one unit. Every time our opponent removes a 16, we remove the other 16 of the pair, and we shall win."

At this a number of boys put their hands up.

"But why do only the powers of two occur? Why not the powers of three or five?"

"I can tell you that, as well. Because every whole number can be expressed as the sum of the powers of two, but not as the sum of powers of three or five. Try it."

The Tak-Tix Game

Two of the boys, Bill and Tom, continued to play the Nimo Game for a while. Then Bill's uncle told them that the Nimo Game has a number of interesting variations. "Such a game is Tak-Tix, best played with coins rather than matches. The coins are placed in a square:

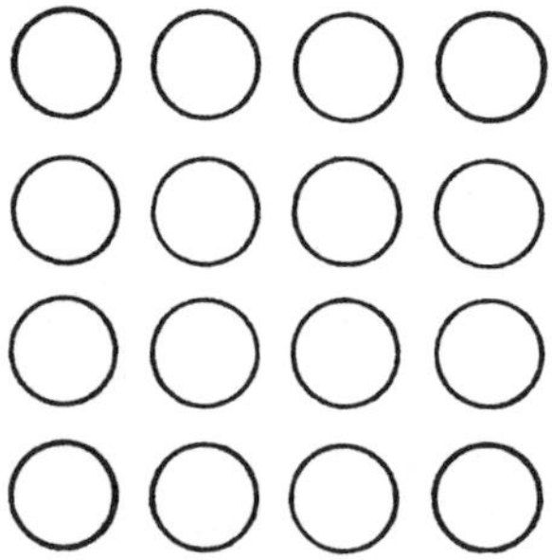

"The players take turns to take coins from any row or column, provided that there is no gap already between the coins to be removed. If, for instance, my partner removes the middle two coins from the first row, I cannot move the first and fourth coins, because there is a gap between them. The person moving the last coin is the loser. If we were to play this so that the person taking away the last coin is the winner, then the game would become too easy, since the solution is obvious."

"Why?" they asked. "Let's try it. Let's put out five rows each containing five coins, like this."

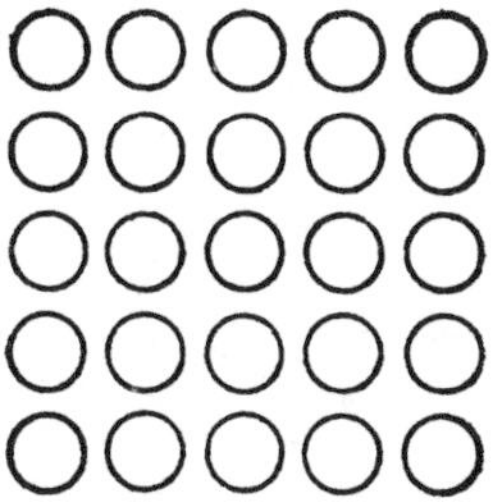

When the coins are arranged like this, there is one coin in the center. Bill, who started, took just this one. Now it was Tom's turn. He took three coins from the fourth row, which were just below the center. Then Bill took the third coin from the second row, which was exactly above the center; that is, he was following the Nimo Game in preserving the symmetry. Since the figure is symmetrical about the center, it is easy to win by removing the last coin.

If there is an even number of rows and columns and, thus, there is no coin at the center, the second player can easily win, because the figure is symmetrical about the two lines running through the center of the square.

The game is much more difficult if the loser is the one who removes the last coin. The theory underlying this version has not yet been worked out by mathematicians.

Six Pennies

Put six pennies on the table, as in the diagram.

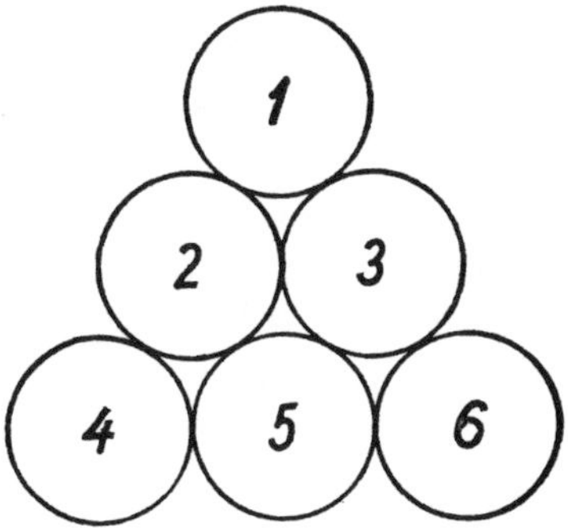

Let us suppose that you can move coins only by sliding them, and also that when one is moved, the others must be left undisturbed.

How many moves do we have to make to rearrange them as below?

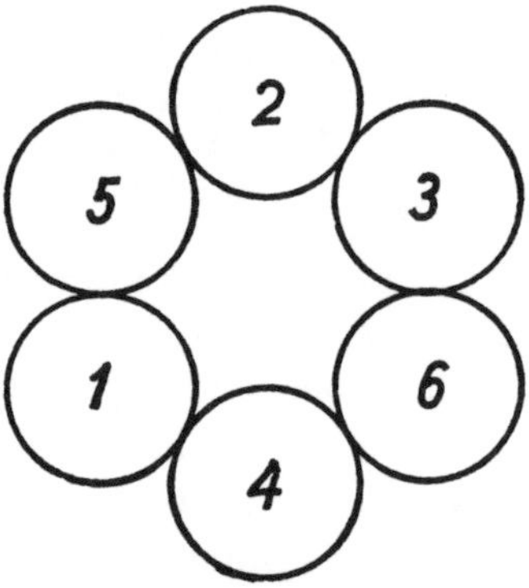

In our drawings we have numbered the coins. Slide coin 1 so that it touches 2 and 4. Then move coin 4 until it touches 5 and 6, then coin 5 below 1 and 2, and finally 1 between coins 4 and 5.

Turn the Dice

The object of the game is for one of the players to reach a given number. Usually a number larger than 20 is chosen.

The first player throws a dice, the sides of which are numbered one to six in the usual way. The next player turns the dice through a quarter rotation in any direction and then adds the number on top to the previous number. The other players have their turns in the same way. The winner is the player who reaches the given number. If anyone gets to a number larger than the given number, he is judged to have lost.

Suppose the target number is 31. Naturally, we can give no way of making sure of winning, because it depends so much on the way the dice lies. But it is possible to work out a way of increasing the chances of winning, or at least stopping another player's chance of victory.

The trick is to reach a number, the remainder of which, after dividing by 9, is the same as when the target figure is divided by 9. The remainder, when 31 is divided by 9, is 4. The only way the player who starts can win is by getting a 4 on the first throw. The players must try to follow the sequence 4, 13, 22, 31, to stop another player winning.

This sequence can be reached if we make sure that our numbers are 5 below the numbers in the sequence. If the number on the top is 5, the next player can turn the dice to 1, 2, 3, 4, or 6. Even if he turns to 4, he has gone one over the number in the sequence; therefore, he can no longer win.

If the first player chooses the target number, then the question is what should be the remainder after dividing by 9, so that he has the greatest chance of winning.

We wondered with which throws the first player can win, if the remainder after dividing by 9 is varied. Our table shows the connection between these two numbers:

Remainder after dividing by 9	*Wins if the first throw is*
1	1 or 5
2	2 or 3
3	3 or 4
4	4
5	5
6	3 or 6
7	2 or 3 or 4
8	4
9	cannot win.

The table shows that there is the best chance of winning if the remainder after dividing by 9 is 7, because then there are three possible throws which lead to victory.

Guess the Throws

Someone threw a dice three times. Paul didn't look, but he guessed the throws. He said this: "Take the number you got in the first throw (4), double it (8), and add 5 (13). Multiply the result by 5 (65) and add the number you got with the second throw (2). To this number (67) add 10 (77) and multiply by 10 (770); finally, add the third number (1), and tell me the final result (771)."

Paul subtracted 350 from this (421), which gave the values of the three throws.

This is how it's done: Call the first throw a, the second b, and the third c. We multiply the first throw by 2, giving $2a$; to this we add 5, that is, $2a + 5$. The result is multiplied by 5: $10a + 25$. To this we add the second throw: $10a + 25 + b$; we add 10: $10a + 35 + b$; multiply by 10: $100a + 350 + 10b$. When we finally add the third throw, c, we get $100a + 10b + c + 350$. Therefore, if we take 350 from the result, the remainder will give us the three numbers thrown.

A Game of Chance

Peter and Paul are playing the following game: Peter throws two dice, and Paul says a number. If the numbers on the dice add up to the number that he said, then Paul wins; otherwise he loses.

Question: What number should Paul say in order that he has the best chance of winning? By how many times should the winner's stake be multiplied, so that the game becomes fair?

Answer: First of all, it is obvious that Paul can say any number between 2 and 12, because the numbers on two dice must add up to at least 2 and not more than 12. We must examine all the possible numbers and then decide on a number which is likely to come up most often, and then we have the best probability of winning.

Let us imagine that the best number to choose is 7.

Let us write down all the possibilities:

If the dice 1 and 2 show

1	1	the total is 2
1	2	the total is 3
2	1	
1	3	the total is 4
2	2	
3	1	
1	4	the total is 5
2	3	
3	2	
4	1	
1	5	the total is 6
2	4	
3	3	
4	2	
5	1	
1	6	the total is 7
2	5	
3	4	
4	3	
5	2	
6	1	

We shall get 8 the same number of times as 6 (five times), 9 as 5 (four times), 10 as 4 (three times), 11 as 3 (twice), and 12 as 2 (once).

The total number of possibilities is therefore 36. If a person always says 7, then there are 6 favorable chances for winning out of 36. The probability of winning is in the ratio of the total number of possibilities and the number of chances: one in six. The game becomes fair if Paul wins six times his stake when the total of the two numbers is 7.

This does not mean that out of 36 throws Paul will win six

times. A probability is not the same as a certainty. But the larger the number of throws, the nearer we shall get to the position that at every sixth throw the numbers on the dice will add up to 7.

Guess the Domino

Charles said that he could guess the number on a domino piece without looking. The others chose one on which there was a 3 on one half and a 5 on the other. Charles then said, "Multiply one number by 5 (15), add 3 (18), double it (36), add to that the second number (41), and tell me the result."

Charles subtracted from the result (41) 6, giving 35, and the numbers gave the number of spots on the two halves of the piece.

We can write this down using symbols: $(5a + 3)2 + b = 10a + b + 6$.

Therefore, if we subtract 6 from the result, we shall get a two-figure number in which the number of tens gives the figure on one half of the domino and the number of units the figure on the other.

Who Is the Loser?

It would be interesting if we found a game for four in which one player was the winner and two of the others were always unable to follow.

This can be done with a 28-piece set, in which the largest piece is the double six.

Each of the four players gets seven pieces. If by chance the first player gets 0-0, 0-1, 0-2, 0-3, 1-4, 1-5, and 1-6 and the fourth 1-1, 1-2, 1-3, 0-4, 0-5, 0-6, and some other piece as the seventh, then the second and third players will not have any pieces with 0 or 1 on them.

The game may then be as follows: The first player starts with the 0-0; the second and third players would not be able to follow; the fourth player could play the 0-4, 0-5, or 0-6 piece. Whatever he plays, the first player will then have his turn, leaving 0 and 1 at the two ends. The second and third players would have to continue "knocking," and the game continues till the fourth player has played his sixth piece. Then the first player plays his seventh piece and wins.

This situation is likely to occur, however, only once in 152,977,968 games.

CHAPTER 6

GAMES FOR ONE

What do we need to play solitaire?

Using a fretsaw, cut out a shape as shown in the diagram; use plywood or something similar. The length of the cross should be about four inches.

Drill a number of holes in this, according to the following diagram.

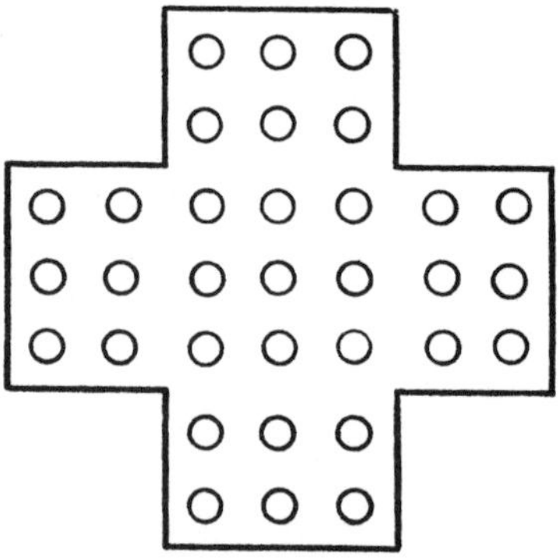

Put a broken match into each hole. The holes should hold the matches firmly upright, and yet they should be easy to remove and replace.

Alternatively, one can buy this game in a toy shop. Every hole except one contains a peg, or "piece."

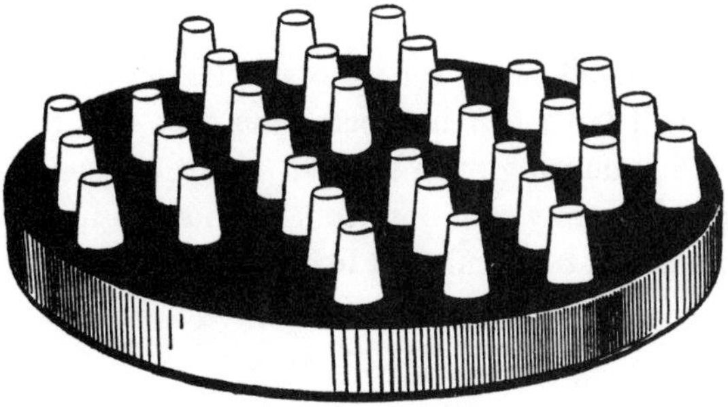

Rules: The game is played by one person only, as in a game of patience. One can move any piece, but only into a vacant place in the same column or row and by jumping over another piece. The piece over which one jumps is removed, and it takes no further part in the game.

With the starting position as shown, only two moves are possible: One moves the second piece either from above or from the right of the vacant place. In either case, one piece is removed; therefore, there will be two vacant places, thereby increasing the number of possible moves.

What sort of games can be set?

Many different games can be played. A simple game is to start with only six pieces arranged in the shape of a cross:

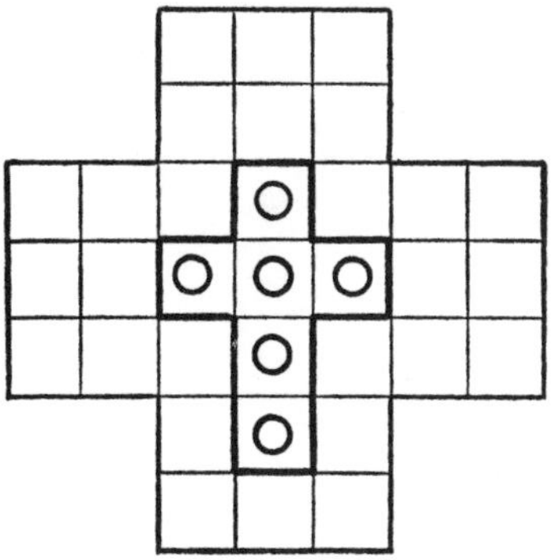

The problem is to end the game by leaving the last piece exactly in the center. Generally, most games of solitaire must end with only one piece being left on the board. That is how the game got its name.

So that we can talk about the various holes, let us number them. Every hole will have two numbers; the first will tell us which column it is in counting from the left, and the second will tell us the number of the row counting from the bottom upward. Therefore, the holes will be numbered like this:

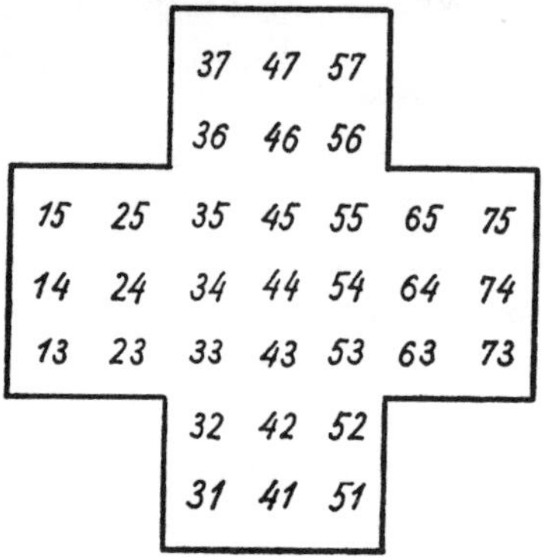

The Cross Game with Six Pieces

We mentioned this problem before. Assume that there are only six pieces on the board, and they are arranged as shown. We must move in such a way that only one piece will be left in position 44.

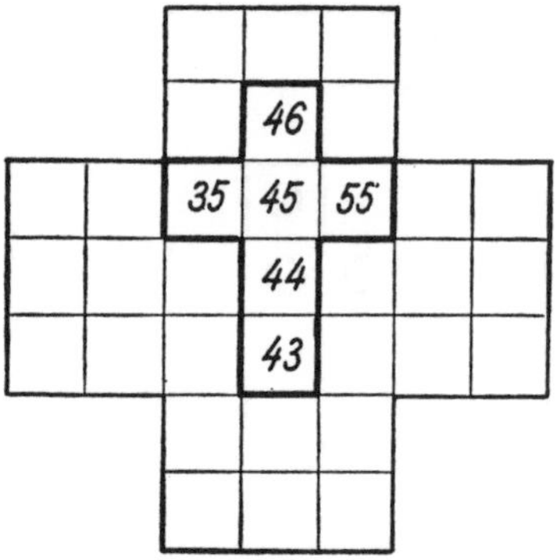

SOLUTION:

Move No. 45 to No. 65 and remove No. 55.
Move No. 43 to No. 45 and remove No. 44.
Move No. 35 to No. 55 and remove No. 45.
Move No. 65 to No. 45 and remove No. 55.
Move No. 46 to No. 44 and remove No. 45.

We are left with only one piece on No. 44.

These moves can be represented as: $\frac{45}{65}$, $\frac{43}{45}$, $\frac{35}{55}$, $\frac{65}{45}$, $\frac{46}{44}$.

The Cross Game with Nine Pieces

Suppose the cross has nine pieces, vertically in positions 42, 43, 44, 45, and 46, and horizontally 24, 34, 44, 54, and 64. Here again the problem is to leave only one piece in hole No. 44.

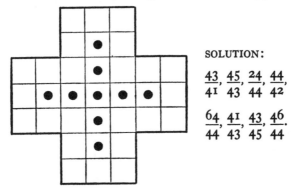

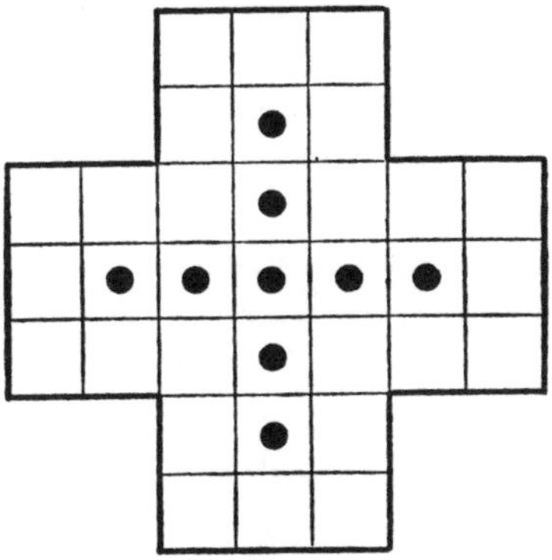

SOLUTION:

$\frac{43}{41}$, $\frac{45}{43}$, $\frac{24}{44}$, $\frac{44}{42}$,

$\frac{64}{44}$, $\frac{41}{43}$, $\frac{43}{45}$, $\frac{46}{44}$.

Triangular game illustrated:

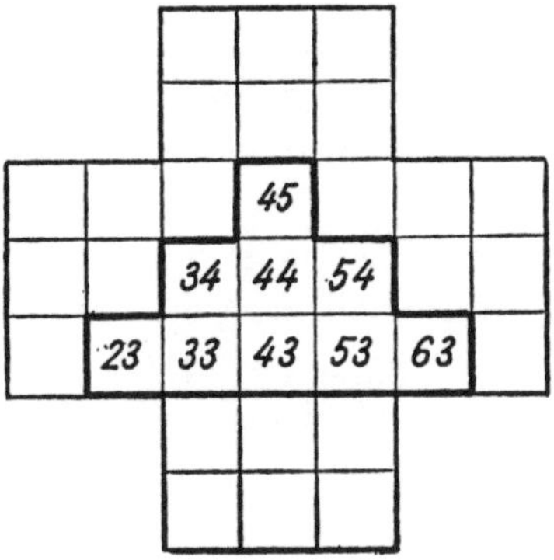

SOLUTION:

$\frac{53}{55}$, $\frac{55}{35}$, $\frac{33}{53}$, $\frac{63}{43}$,

$\frac{44}{42}$, $\frac{35}{33}$, $\frac{23}{43}$, $\frac{42}{44}$.

The Real Game of Solitaire

The games we have been playing up till now were only warming-up exercises. The real game involves having a piece in every hole but one and having to remove all but one. For example, at the start there are pieces in every hole except in hole 64. We must remove all the pieces till we end up with one only, in hole 24.

Now, this is much more difficult, since we have to deal with 32 pieces, whereas up till now we have been playing with only six or nine.

How many problems does this represent?

Not only do we have to deal with many more pieces, but also the problem of starting with only one vacant hole and ending up with only one piece can be approached in many different ways. Since there are 33 holes and the final piece can be in any one of 33 different places, this represents $33 \times 33 = 1{,}089$ problems. It takes some time to solve only one, but this number will be quite a test of patience. We shall now attempt to apply logic to this "jungle."

Group the holes according to their position.

The solitaire board is symmetrical in many ways; therefore, there are "similar" holes on it. For instance, all the corner holes: 31, 51, 73, 75, 57, 37, 15, and 13. These eight corner holes belong to one group being all similar to one another.

Also 32, 52, 63, 65, 56, 36, 25, and 23 are similar because they are in the middle of the outer row in each limb of the cross. In the above two groups there are sixteen holes. Also, there are four other groups each containing four similar holes:

Finally, hole 44 remains, which does not resemble any other.

In this way we get seven groups. Since the members of a group resemble one another, we can take the first in a group as a representative of that group of holes. This makes the task a bit easier. Therefore, the empty hole with which we start can occupy one of seven positions: 31, 32, 41, 42, 33, 43, or 44.

Already we have some means of organizing the number of possibilities. However, it is not as easy as all that, because there are so many different places at which the game can end. Can one be sure of finishing the game in a predetermined hole when starting from one particular hole? Or perhaps where you finish depends on where you start? In other words, are there problems in this game – as in other games – which can be solved and others which cannot?

We should answer these questions instead of laboriously trying out all the possible solutions to all the problems.

Notice what the holes represent. What does a move in the game actually mean? In every move, three holes next to another are taking part, and all the three have different roles. We move a piece from one, we put this piece in another, and we move a piece from the third. The holes can have different roles on different occasions. We may move a piece from one hole, only to put another piece there later. One thing is certain: Three neighboring holes – beside or below one another – are involved, each having a different role. So that we can examine this more closely, it would be helpful if we could distinguish between them. Let us assume that we have painted the holes with different colors – the first one red, the second green, and the third blue. All the holes in the board must be painted so that three holes next to one another are painted in the three different colors. We can do this if the holes lying on a diagonal are painted with the same color. The diagonals running parallel will all be painted with a different color. The coloring can be represented as:

		R	G	B		
		B	R	G		
B	R	G	B	R	G	B
G	B	R	G	B	R	G
R	G	B	R	G	B	R
		G	B	R		
		R	G	B		

R = red
G = green
B = blue

Previously we gave the holes in the board numbers. Let us have a look how the colors and the numbers are connected.

According to colors, the holes can be divided as:

reds	13	31	25	34	43	52	37	46	55	64	73
greens	14	23	32	41	35	44	53	47	56	65	74
blues	15	24	33	42	51	36	45	54	63	57	75

Adding the two digits in each number, we get:

reds	4	4	7	7	7	7	10	10	10	10	10
greens	5	5	5	5	8	8	8	11	11	11	11
blues	6	6	6	6	6	9	9	9	9	12	12

The reds have numbers which if divided by three give a remainder of one, the greens two, and the blues zero.

What happens with the groups as we play?

We remove a piece from a hole; that color, therefore, loses a piece. We put the piece in another hole; that color gains a piece. The piece over which we jumped is removed; therefore, that color loses a piece. If, for example, we remove a piece from a red hole and jump over a green hole and land in a blue hole, the red and green groups each lose a piece and the blue group gains one.

How does the number of pieces in a color group change during a move?

Let us have a look at an example. Suppose that the red group contains 5, the green 8, and the blue 9 pieces. Suppose also that we move a piece from a blue hole to a red one, jumping over a green hole. Then the number of pieces in the three groups will be 6, 7, 8. Compare these with the original numbers. Every one of them has changed, yet something has remained the same. What is it?

When we started, the number of pieces in the red group was odd, in the green group even, and in the blue group odd. Even numbers when divided by two give zero as a remainder. Looking at the numbers as either even or odd, the number in the green group was different from the numbers in the red and blue groups.

After the move, the number of red pieces became even, the green odd, and the blue even. This is obvious, since each number merely changed by one. Looking at these numbers from an even-odd point of view, the number of reds and blues is similar, whereas the number of greens is different.

Those numbers which were similar – as odd or even numbers – before a move remain similar afterward, and those which were different before remain different.

We can try this any number of times but we shall always get the same result. This is natural, since the number in each group during a move changes by one, the odd numbers becoming even and the evens becoming odd.

If this is true for one move, it must be equally true for the whole game. The number in two of the three color groups must be similar and the remaining one different from an even-odd point of view. Those which resembled each other to start with resemble each other at the end, and the one that was different at the start will remain so.

Therefore, if at the start the number of pieces in the red holes is odd and the number in the blue and green holes is even, then at the end the red one will be different from the other two. From this it follows that not all problems in the game of solitaire can be solved, but only those which will conform to this rule.

How many end games are there?

Now we will have a look at how a game of solitaire approaches its end. It could happen that all the holes of one color are empty and there is one piece in each of the other two groups. There can be only one move left; one piece steps over the other and the latter is removed. Now only one piece remains, and no more moves are possible. One color has one piece and the others none. This can be shown as: 1, 0, 0.

There could be another ending. One might reach a situation where all the three groups have one piece each. Then one piece can step over another, and the middle one is removed. This game would end with one color having two pieces and the others none, and the number of pieces in each group is 2, 0, 0

In the first case, the number of pieces in each group is odd, even, even. (We regard zero as even, since if we divide it by two the remainder is zero.) Those starting positions where two color-group numbers are similar and the other is different end like this. In the second case, all the three numbers at the end are even; therefore, at the start all three must have been even or all three must have been odd.

Which is the most difficult game?

The game where all the holes except one at the start are full and at the end only one piece must remain will always be the most difficult. The three groups of holes all have the same number of pieces, 11. But two groups have 11 pieces and the third 10. The starting situation is odd, odd, even. Two are similar, but the third one is different. This situation must stay the same throughout the game. This starting position must lead at the end to 1, 0, 0, because two colors are similar. The color which is "different" at the start will remain "different" at the end. If at the start one red hole had no piece in it, then at the end a red hole will contain one. The other problems cannot be solved; even an infinite amount of patience is no help.

Therefore, it is worth tackling only those problems where an empty hole at the start is the same color as the one we wish to have filled at the end.

Color the solitaire board a second time.

This still represents a large number of problems, as one starting position, if the piece is in a red hole, can give 11 different endings. So that we can reduce the possible endings even further, we can paint the solitaire board once again so that we have lines of colors running at right angles to the previous lines. The result is that each hole will have two colors:

		RB	GG	BR		
		BG	RR	GB		
BB	RG	GR	BB	RG	GR	BB
GG	BR	RB	GG	BR	RB	GG
RR	GB	BG	RR	GB	BG	RR
		GR	BB	RG		
		RB	GG	BR		

The rules that we formulated before still apply; the empty hole at the start must belong to the same group of colors as the hole the final piece will occupy.

How to organize the problems which can be solved.

Can a problem which obeys the even–odd rule still remain impossible to solve? Could it be that they will remain impossible because they do not obey some other rule? We must have a closer look at some examples.

We have seen that the empty hole at the start can be in seven different positions: 31, 32, 41, 42, 33, 43, and 44.

According to their color grouping: red, 31 and 43; green, 41, 44, and 32; and blue, 42 and 33.

What happens if the vacant hole is 31? This number (31) on the twice-colored board has the colors blue-red; therefore, the end position which belongs to it must also be blue–red. These are 31, 34, 37, and 64.

We can find the possible endings with other starting positions also.

Starting at	*Finishing at*
31	31, 34, 37, 64
32	32, 35, 65
41	41, 44, 47, 14, 74
42	42, 45, 15, 75
33	33, 36, 63
43	43, 46, 13, 73
44	44, 41, 47, 14, 74

We have managed to reduce the number of possibilities from $33 \times 33 = 1{,}089$ to 28. If you look still closer, you will see that some of these are the same. For example, holes 14 and 74 are symmetrical when looked at from 41. Similarly, from 42, numbers 15 and 75 are the same; from 33, numbers 36 and 63; from 43, numbers 13 and 73; from 44, numbers 47, 14, and 74. Finally there are only 21 possible games left.

We can also see that if the starting and finishing positions are changed around, the game remains substantially the same.

The remaining possible games can be reduced still further. Let us draw diagrams of these, in which we represent the starting positions as little circles and the endings with dots:

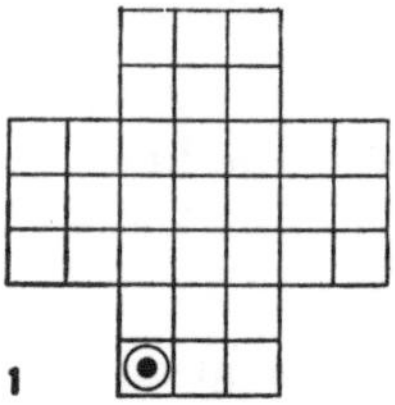
1

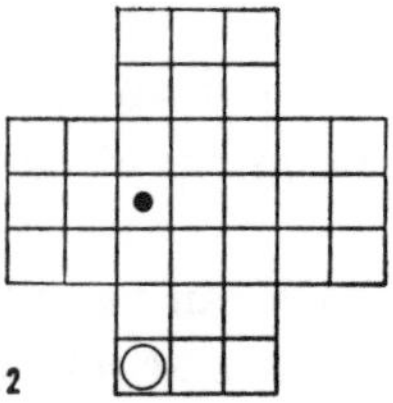
2

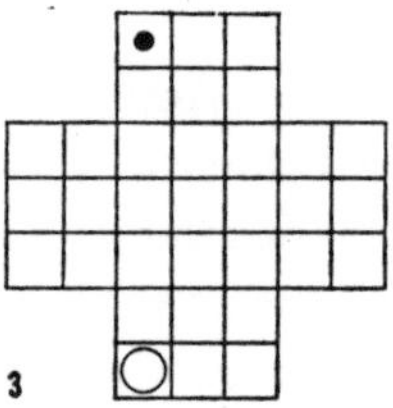
3

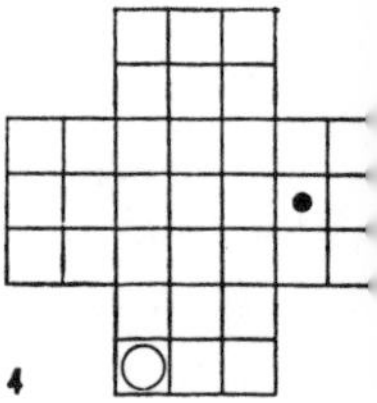
4

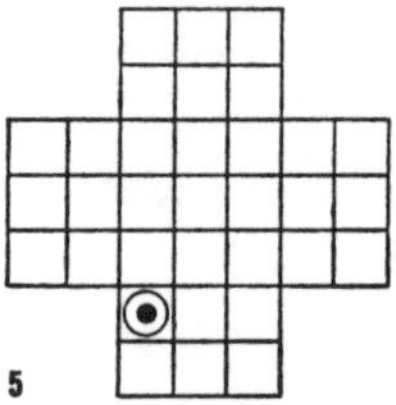
5

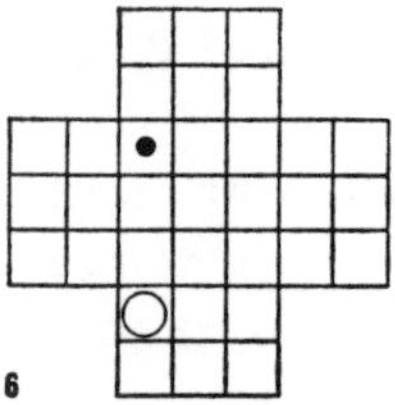
6

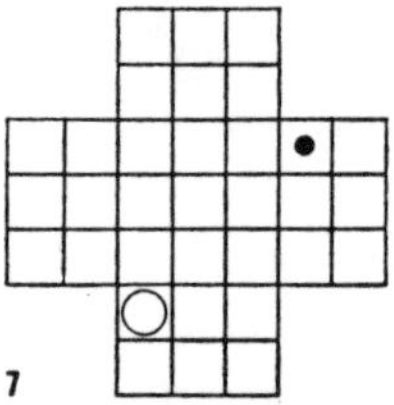
7

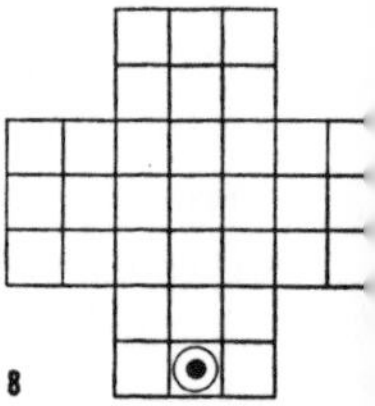
8

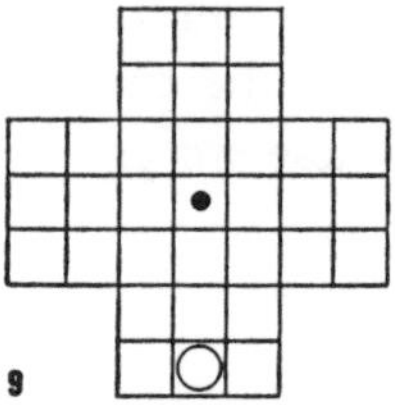
9

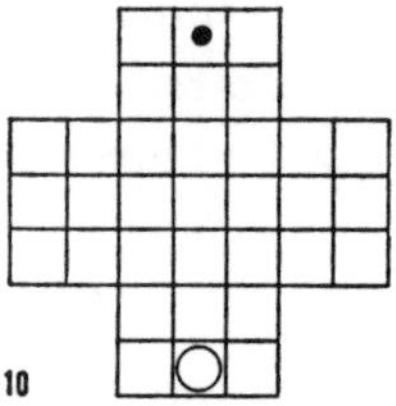
10

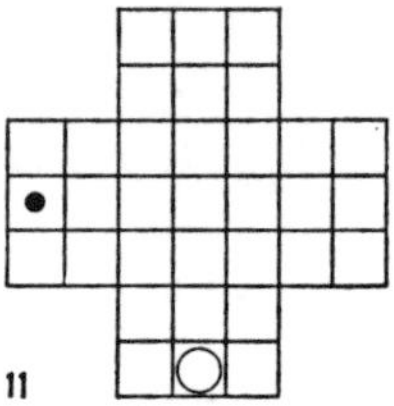
11

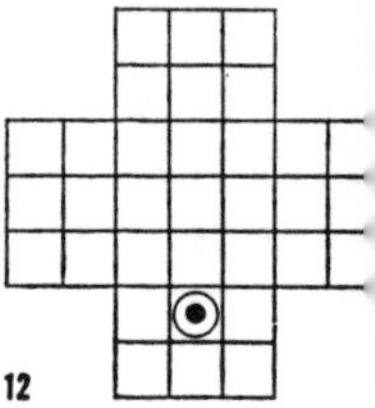
12

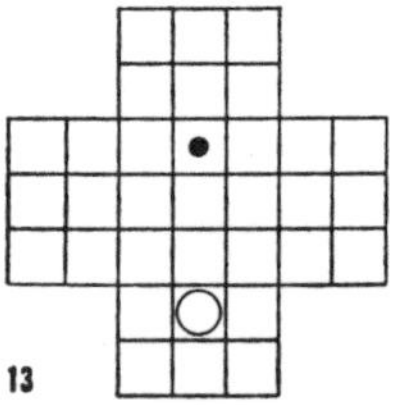
13

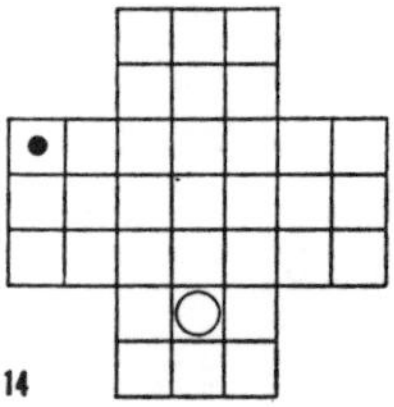
14

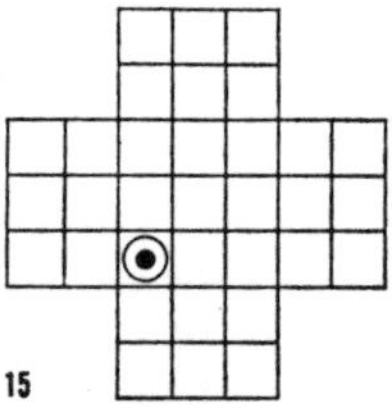
15

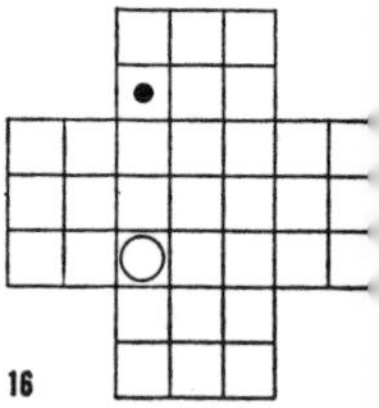
16

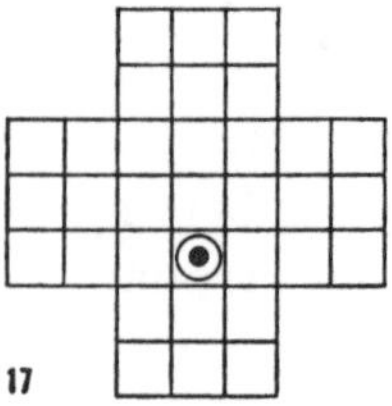
17

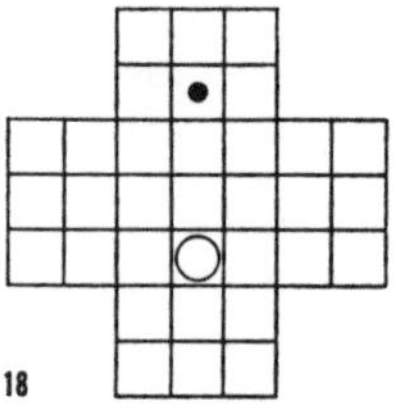
18

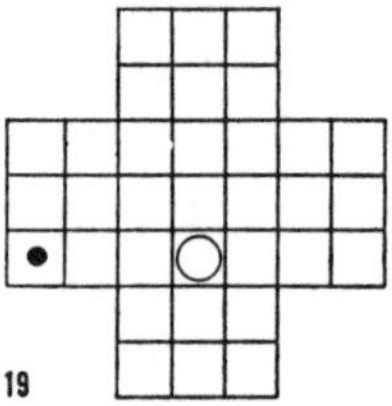
19

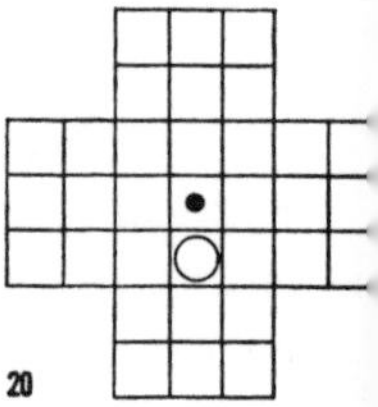
20

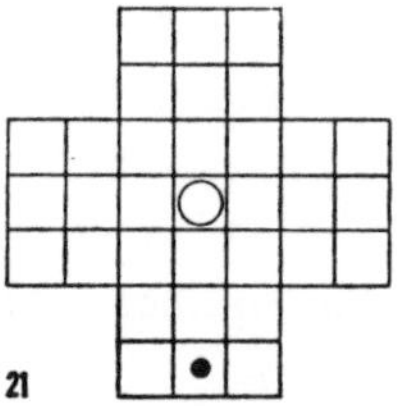
21

We notice that Fig. 2 is the same as Fig. 19, only turned 90 degrees; also the same are 4 and 14, 6 and 16, 9 and 21, and 13 and 18; therefore we need solve only 16 problems.

Mathematicians who founded the theory for solitaire examined the 16 possible games. Without playing them right through, certain rules suggested themselves. The solutions to those games which were possible to play right through were gathered together in book form so that it was possible to look them up as one looks up a word in a dictionary.

The examination of the 16 types clearly indicated *that if the vacant hole with which we started and the hole in which we wish to have the last piece belong to the same group in a board which was painted twice, the whole game can be played successfully.*

Now, the only thing that is needed is some easy way of remembering in which places we can finish when we start with a certain vacant hole.

It is not our intention to give any "rule" which can be learned "by heart" – the diagrams are too numerous to be remembered, and the coloring method is rather laborious. There is an easily remembered and amusing method of doing this.

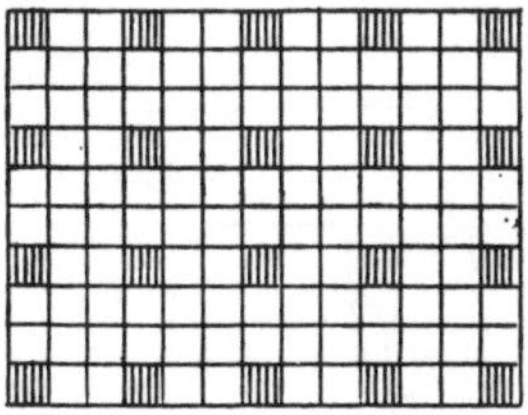

Cut out a rectangle from cardboard. Divide the rectangle into squares of the same size as the area of one hole on the solitaire board. Cut out one of these small squares; then cut out the third square from this which lies both horizontally and vertically. The grid we get from this is placed over the vacant hole with which we intend to start, and the other "windows" show the possible endings.

CHAPTER 7

GAMES FOR TWO

In Chapter 5 we introduced you to the Nimo Game. We shall show you how the type of thinking used in that game can be used in another game. In general, we can say that if in a game the winner is the person who does something last and the game can be divided into two identical halves, then the second person to start can always win.

The "move" can mean all sorts of things. We shall show some of them.

Game with Cigars

Two rich industrialists were sitting on either side of a square table. One of them put an ordinary cigar on the table, which looks like this:

Then the second one put a similar cigar on the table as well. They continued doing this, and the winner was the one who put the last cigar on the table, making sure that no two cigars touched each other.

We shall suppose that each player had an unlimited supply of identical cigars.

If we want to use the principle we mentioned above, we must consider how the game could be divided into two symmetrical halves. As the table is square in shape, this is quite an easy task, since a square is symmetrical about its two diagonals, and the two lines connecting the middle of opposite sides. If – in theory only – we divide the table into two symmetrical sides, the second player should place his cigar in a position symmetrical to the first player's cigar.

To find symmetrical positions about a single axis is relatively easy; a few examples are shown in our diagram.

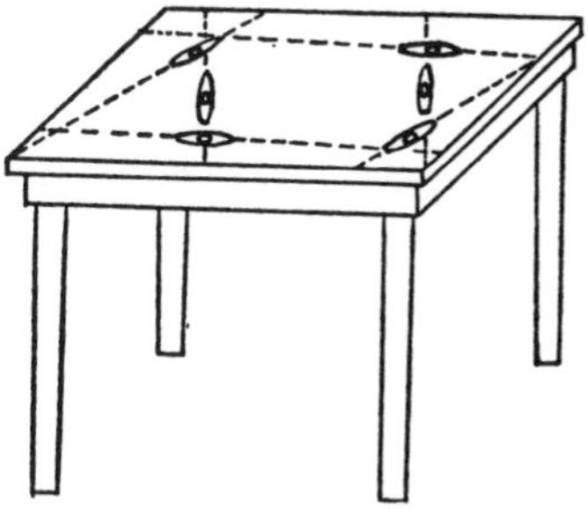

But a square is also symmetrical about its center, where both the diagonals and the lines connecting the middle of opposite sides meet.

We can get two symmetrical points about the center by connecting one of them with the center and measuring the distance of the first point from the center on the other side. This is shown in the diagram.

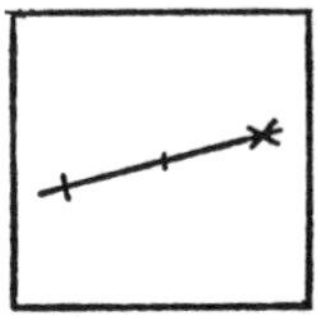

As long as the first player can find a space, so will the second; therefore, the second player will win. There is one exception – if the first player stands a cigar on its end exactly on the center point. The center is symmetrical only with itself, and that is already taken!

Due to the finite size of the table, there is no need for an inexhaustible supply of cigars, and anyway, children are not usually allowed to play with cigars. The game can also be played with small pieces of paper on a larger paper square.

Game of Square

Two players take turns to pencil in a side of one of the small squares. If one of them comes across a square where the three sides have been drawn in, then he can complete it and put in the middle his sign, an o or a 1. The winner is the player with the most squares.

If both players are playing carefully and both of them are familiar with the principles of symmetry, then the second player will complete a square of his own first.

The rules also say that when this happens, the player who gets a square has another turn; therefore, he is now the first player and has a relatively unfavorable position. He can get back to being the second player by deliberately giving a square to his opponent, but he must be careful not to give away too great an advantage.

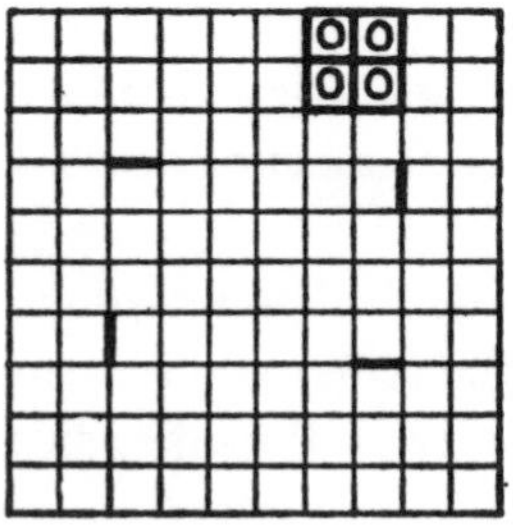

She Loves Me, She Loves Me Not

The question of symmetry is also involved in a little game we sometimes play with flowers in the summer. Sam Lloyd, the well-known American author, who became famous through writing about mathematics, described how he was once on holiday in the Swiss Alps. While crossing a meadow full of flowers, he met a little peasant girl. The writer picked a daisy and offered to tell the girl's future. They took turns to pull off one of the flower's petals;

if the girl were to pull off the last petal, then she would get married, but if only the bare stalk is left for her, then she would remain single. The girl quickly dismissed the game; it was well known among the girls in the village, and they had changed it a bit. The players were allowed to pull off either one or two petals at a time. The mathematician began to play, and much to his amazement, the girl won every time. She always tried to give the flower a symmetrical appearance, in other words, to divide the flower into two symmetrical halves. Only the first move really needed thought; if, for example, the flower had thirteen petals and the first player tore off one, then she pulled off two from the opposite side of the flower. If the first player pulled off two, then she tore off one on the opposite side.

In both cases two symmetrical groups remain, with five petals in each group. Then it is merely a question of following the first player's move until "victory" is achieved.

Ticktacktoe

The advantage of this game is that it is quite simple and requires only pencil and paper. One player's sign is O and the other's X. Two horizontal and two vertical lines form the "board."

These form nine squares, into which the players write in turn. Each tries to write his sign into three squares vertically, horizontally, or diagonally. The first one to achieve this is the winner. So the purpose of the game is twofold: to achieve one's own aim and to stop one's opponent from reaching his.

The complete theory of the game takes up more space than we can give in this book. For this reason we shall not be discussing it in great detail. This much is clear: the first player can make one of three moves:

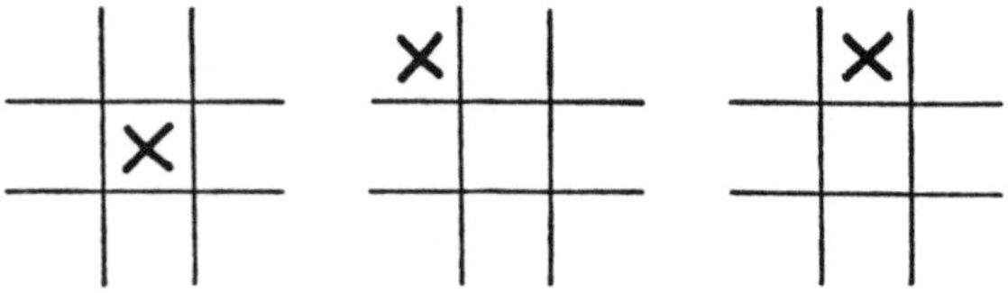

The best moves to counter these are:

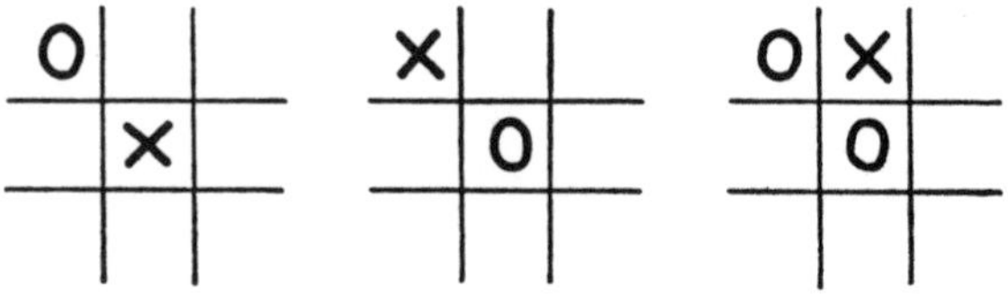

The rest we will leave to you, the players, since the whole game is very short.

Battleships

This game needs only pencil and paper, like the previous one. Both players draw two 10 × 10 squares on squared paper. Then they put numbers and letters against the squares, as below:

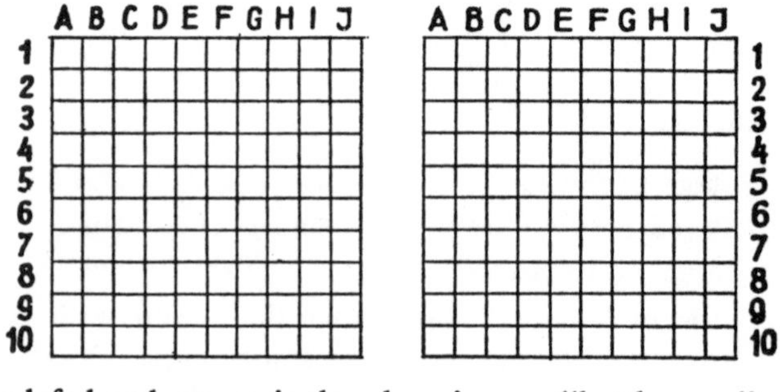

The left-hand square is the player's own "battle area," and the right-hand one that of the opponent.

Each player draws four "ships" into his own squares: one

battleship (5 squares), one cruiser (3 squares), and two destroyers (2 squares each). Their exact position is naturally kept secret from the opponent! Now the "battle" starts. The first player has seven "shots"; he tells his opponent the letter and number of each square where the shots have landed. The second player notes where all the seven have fallen and then tells his opponent which of the shots are hits and which are misses, and if they are hits, what sort of ships were hit. The first player records the hits and misses in his right-hand-side square.

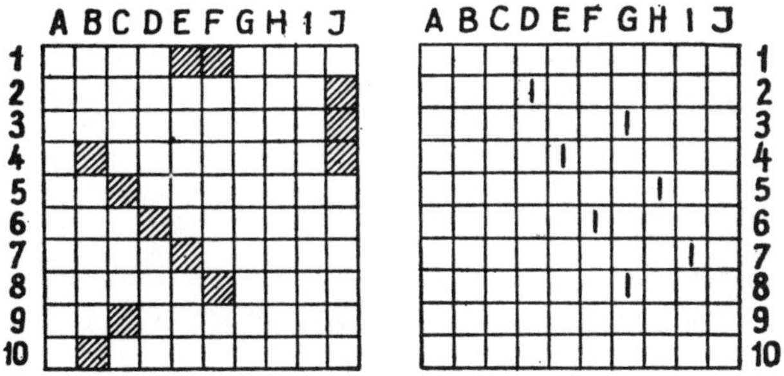

From the position of the hits and the size of the ship hit, with a bit of thought one can deduce where the rest of the ships are. The object is to score hits on all the ships.

Now the second player has seven "shots," similarly noting the position of hits and misses. They take turns until a ship has been destroyed. Then the number of "shots" is reduced by five, three, or two, according to the size of the ship destroyed. The player who first loses all his ships has lost. This game obviously depends on how skillfully the player has placed his ships. After complicated calculations of probabilities, it has been worked out that the safest place for a battleship is a corner and the least safe position is in the center of a square.

CHAPTER 8

PROBLEMS THROUGH THE AGES

In this chapter we shall show you a few problems which interested people in the past. Some of them occur again and again in old mathematical books.

Some French Problems

The following few examples occurred first in French books written by Chuquet (1484) and Clarius (1608):

1. Someone has a sum of money, $\frac{1}{3}$ of which he spends. $\frac{2}{3}$ of the remainder he loses at dice, leaving 12 ducats in his pocket. How much money did he have originally?

SOLUTION: If he spent $\frac{1}{3}$, he had $\frac{2}{3}$ left. He lost $\frac{2}{3}$ of the remainder at dice; $\frac{2}{3}$ of $\frac{2}{3}$ is $\frac{4}{9}$. Therefore, he spent and lost $\frac{1}{3} + \frac{4}{9} = \frac{7}{9}$. The remainder is $\frac{2}{9} = 12$. If $\frac{2}{9}$ of the money is 12, then the original sum must have been 54.

The problem can also be solved by drawing a diagram, without calculation at all.

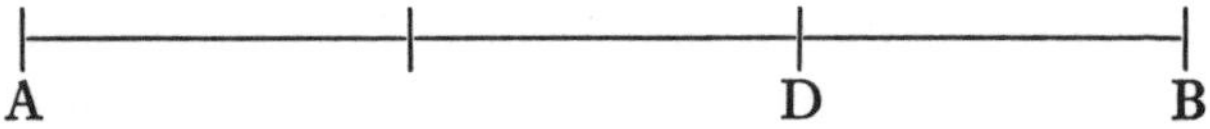

Let us call the unknown sum AB. The sum corresponding to DB was spent. We divide the remainder into three equal parts:

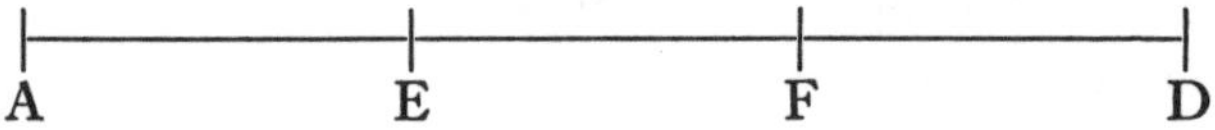

AE = 12, and ED was lost at dice. If AE = 12, then AD, three times AE, must equal 36. DB, half of AD, is then 18. The total is $36 + 18 = 54$ ducats.

2. A length of cloth was dyed as follows: $\frac{1}{3}$ and $\frac{1}{4}$ were dyed black and the remaining 8 yards gray. What was the total length of the cloth?

SOLUTION: $\frac{1}{3} + \frac{1}{4}$ is $\frac{7}{12}$. Therefore, the remaining 8 yards must be $\frac{5}{12}$ of the total. It follows then that $\frac{1}{12} = \frac{8}{5}$ yards, that is, $\frac{12}{12}$ is $12 \times \frac{8}{5} = 19\frac{1}{5}$ yards.

3. A merchant went to three markets. He doubled his money at the first and spent 30 ducats. At the second he trebled his money and spent 54 ducats, and at the third he multiplied his money by four and spent 72 ducats, and yet he had 48 ducats left. How much did he start with?

SOLUTION: Let us start from the end and work toward the beginning. He had 48 ducats left. Previously he spent 72 ducats; therefore, before he spent that, he must have had $72 + 48 = 120$ ducats. This was four times the sum he had before that: $120 \div 4 = 30$. After the second market, this must have been 54 more, that is, 84 ducats. Before the second market he had only a third of this, that is, 28; before that, $28 + 30 = 58$; half of this is 29 ducats.

4. A servant received 100 ducats wages and a suit of clothes for a year's work. One year, however, he left after only seven months of the year had elapsed, and he got his suit of clothes and 20 ducats. How much was the suit worth?

SOLUTION: After seven months the amount due to the servant was $\frac{7}{12}$ of 100 ducats and $\frac{7}{12}$ of the cost of the suit.

He did not get all the money due to him, but a little less. The difference between what he got and what he should have gotten is $\frac{5}{12}$ of the cost of the suit:

$$\frac{7}{12} \times 100 = \frac{700}{12}; \frac{700}{12} - 20 = \frac{700 - 240}{12} = \frac{460}{12}$$

$\frac{5}{12}$ of the cost of the suit is $\frac{460}{12}$; $\frac{1}{12}$ is then $\frac{92}{12}$; therefore, the suit is worth 92 ducats.

5. Two wine merchants arrived at the gates of Paris. One had 64 and the other 20 barrels of wine. However, they did not have enough money to pay the keeper of the gate. The first paid 40 francs and 5 barrels of wine. The second paid 2 barrels of wine but received 40 francs in change. What was the value of a barrel of wine, and what did the gatekeeper charge on each barrel?

SOLUTION:

Price of 5 barrels + 40 francs = duty on 64 barrels of wine; and
Price of 2 barrels − 40 francs = duty on 20 barrels of wine.

Adding these we get:

Price of 7 barrels = duty on 84 barrels of wine; or
Price of 1 barrel = duty on 12 barrels of wine.

Now, we know that the duty on 12 barrels is the same as the price of one barrel. Therefore, in the first line above, we can write instead of the price of 5 barrels, 5×12 = duty on 60 barrels of wine.

Then, the duty on 60 barrels + 40 francs = the duty on 64 barrels of wine, or the duty on 1 barrel = 10 francs, and so the price of a barrel is 120 francs.

Some Greek Problems

A book called *Greek Anthology*, which survived the Middle Ages, contains several trick questions of this sort. We shall show you some of them:

1. The statue of Pallas Athene had the following inscription on it (the original was in verse, but here it is given in prose): "I, Pallas, am made of pure gold, which was donated by the poets. Half was given by Kariseus, an eighth by Thespian. Solon gave a tenth, and Themison a twentieth. Nine talents' worth of gold were still needed, and Aristodikos gave that." How much gold did the statue contain?

SOLUTION: $\frac{1}{2} + \frac{1}{8} + \frac{1}{10} + \frac{1}{20}$, that is, $\frac{31}{40}$ of the required gold was available, $\frac{9}{40}$ of the gold was still needed. This was given by Aristodikos, and it came to 9 talents' worth. Therefore, the total gold in the statue must have been 40 talents' worth.

2. According to legend, Euclid was the author of the following: A mule and a donkey are struggling with a load of sacks. The donkey was groaning, so the mule said to him: "Why do you complain? If you gave me one sack, I would have twice as many as

you, and if I gave you one of my sacks, then we would be carrying equal loads." How many sacks did each have?

SOLUTION: If the mule gave one sack to the donkey the situation would be:

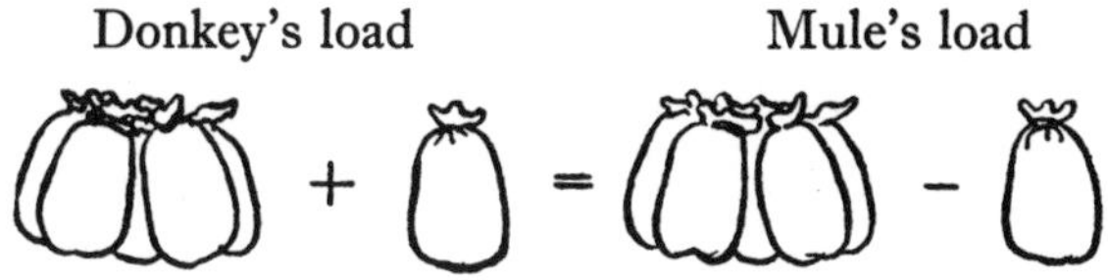

The mule therefore is carrying two sacks more than the donkey:

If the donkey gives one sack to the mule, then the position is:

Now the mule is carrying four more sacks than the donkey. As the mule's load is twice that of the donkey, the difference of four sacks must be equal to the load that the donkey is now carrying. The donkey therefore had four sacks and the mule eight after they changed loads.

Originally the donkey had five and the mule seven sacks.

3. On the grave of Diophantes, the Alexandrian mathematician, the following inscription appears (in the original it was in verse, but here it is given in prose):

> This stone marks the grave of Diophantes.
> If you solve this riddle, you will know his age.
> He spent one-sixth of his life as a child,
> Then one-twelfth as a youth.
> He was married for one-seventh of his life.
> Five years after he married, his son was born.

Fate overtook his beloved child; he died
When he was half the age of his father.
Four more years did the father live
Before reaching the end of this life.

How long did Diophantes live?

SOLUTION: First let us add those parts which are given as fractions: $\frac{1}{6}+\frac{1}{12}+\frac{1}{7}+\frac{1}{2}=\frac{14+7+12+42}{84}=\frac{75}{84}$.

From the whole life, $\frac{9}{84}$ is left unaccounted for. We are told, however, of $4+5=9$ years. From this, then, we can say that 1 year is $\frac{1}{84}$ of the mathematician's life. So the answer is that Diophantes lived to the ripe old age of 84.

4. Polykrates, the moneylender, said to Pythagoras, the scientist: "Blessed Pythagoras, source of muses, answer my question! How many wise scholars live in your house?"

This is what Pythagoras answered: "Here is my answer, great Polykrates! Half of the scholars are dedicated to writing books, one-quarter are dedicated to studying the wonders of nature, and one-seventh contemplate in silence. Three women complete the household. Now you can easily calculate how many of us there are."

Can we help Polykrates?

SOLUTION: We can get the number of people living in the house in this way: A half, a quarter, and a seventh added together give $\frac{25}{28}$ of the total. The remainder – three women – must be $\frac{3}{28}$ of the total. Therefore, there must have been 28 people in the household.

5. The three Graces were carrying baskets of apples, each basket having the same number of apples in it. They met the nine Muses, who asked them for some apples. Each of the Graces gave away the same number of apples, and in the end all the Graces and all the Muses had the same number of apples.

How many apples were there in the baskets, and how many were given to each Muse?

SOLUTION: The interesting part of this problem is that in theory it has a large number of solutions. Let us suppose that each of the Graces had four apples. Each gives three to the Muses, and so they will each have one. But we get another correct answer if we suppose that each basket contained eight apples, six of which were given to the Muses, and so they all end up having two apples.

Continuing this process, each basket can have any multiple of four. This, in general, can be written as $4n$. Since there are three Graces, the total number of apples is $3 \times 4n = 12n$. If we divide this into twelve equal portions, each portion will have n apples. In the first example, $n = 1$ (every basket had $4 \times 1 = 4$ apples) and in the second $n = 2$. When $n = 3$, each basket would contain 12 apples, and so on.

We can ask why the multiples of 4? Because the three Graces and the nine Muses form four groups of three.

Obviously there must be a limit to the number of apples, as the three Graces cannot carry an infinite number, but this does not concern us here.

Ancient Arabian Riddle

A hunter was hunting alone and he was running short of food. Luckily he met two shepherds, one of whom had three small loaves and the other five. When the hunter asked them for food, they agreed to divide the loaves equally among the three of them. The hunter thanked them for the food and paid the shepherds 8 piasters.

How did the shepherds divide the money?

SOLUTION: If one were to answer without thinking, he would say the first shepherd had 3 piasters and the second 5. After a little thought, one would realize that this is not correct. Why?

The 8 piasters was in payment for $\frac{8}{3}$ loaves. It follows, then, that the equivalent of 8 loaves is 24 piasters, or one loaf is worth 3 piasters. Since each ended up with $2\frac{2}{3}$ loaves, the first shepherd, who had three loaves to start with, gave $\frac{1}{3}$ of a loaf to the hunter; the other $2\frac{1}{3}$ was given by the other shepherd. Therefore, 1 piaster goes to the first shepherd and 7 to the second.

An Old Hindu Riddle

Three travelers stopped at an inn and asked for supper. The innkeeper could offer only baked potatoes. While the potatoes were baking, the travelers fell asleep. Soon one of them woke up, saw the dish of potatoes, and took a third of them without waking the others. Later the second one woke up, saw the dish, and ate a third of the remaining potatoes. Later the third one did the same. When all three were sleeping once again, the innkeeper cleared the table and found 8 potatoes left.

How many were there to start with?

SOLUTION: The first traveler ate a $\frac{1}{3}$, leaving $\frac{2}{3}$ of the original number. The second one ate $\frac{1}{3}$ of this, that is $\frac{2}{9}$ of the original, leaving $\frac{2}{3} - \frac{2}{9} = \frac{4}{9}$ of the original. The third one ate $\frac{1}{3}$ of this, that is, $\frac{4}{27}$, leaving $\frac{4}{9} - \frac{4}{27} = \frac{8}{27}$ of the original. But since the remainder is 8, the original number must have been 27.

The same result can be obtained by a drawing:

oooo	The third traveler left 8 potatoes.
oooo	This could have been only if he found 12 and ate a third.
ooo ooo	This was left by the second traveler after he ate a third.
ooo ooo	Therefore, he found 18 on the plate.
ooo ooo	The first traveler left 18 potatoes; he must have
ooo ooo	eaten 9. The innkeeper must have baked 27
ooo ooo	potatoes.

CHAPTER 9

GAMES WITH GEOMETRY

George and Steven are brothers, both very keen on mathematics. It's too early to say who is the cleverer, because George is only 16 and Steven is just 14. Because he is two years younger, Steven looks up to George, and George tends to exploit this. George takes great pride in telling Steven all the "great" things he has been doing at school.

One day Steven rushes in, all excited. "We've been learning all about Pythagoras' theorem today! It won't be just a secret between you and your friends anymore. I know now that in all right-angled triangles the area of the square on the hypotenuse is equal to the sum of the squares on the other two sides."

George was impressed by his enthusiasm and replied carefully: "You said that very well! But how do you know that this applies to *all* right-angled triangles?"

"We measured it! In class every boy drew a right-angled triangle on squared paper; we all constructed squares on the three sides

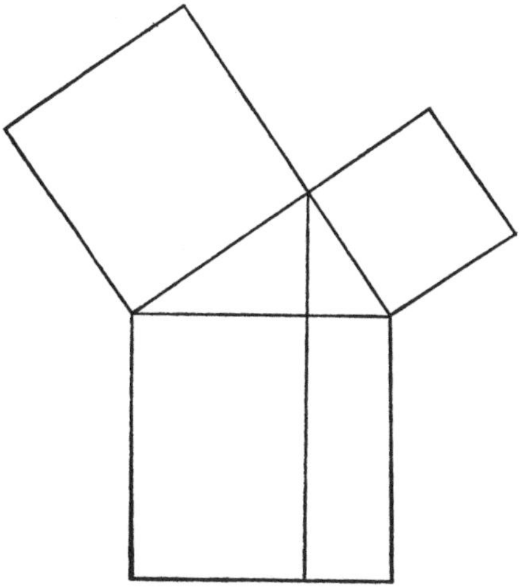

and measured the areas of the squares. We found that, in every case, the sum of the areas of the two smaller squares was equal to the area of the larger square."

"There's more to it than that!" replied George. "Unless one can prove it, other than by measuring, there might be a number of right-angled triangles where this was not so. I'll show you how to prove it.

"Drop a perpendicular onto the longest side and extend it. In this way the square on the longest side is divided into two rectangles. The area of the rectangle on the right is equal to that of the square to the right of it, and the area of the rectangle on the left is equal to that of the square to the left."

"Really? That's marvelous! If this is so, then the sum of the areas of the two smaller squares would really be equal to the area of the larger square. Show me how one can prove this?"

"I will incline the square a little; its area will not change, because if we take the triangle BCF from the trapezium ABFD, the square remains. If we take the triangle ADE (which equals BCF), the parallelogram is left unchanged. If I incline the rectangle

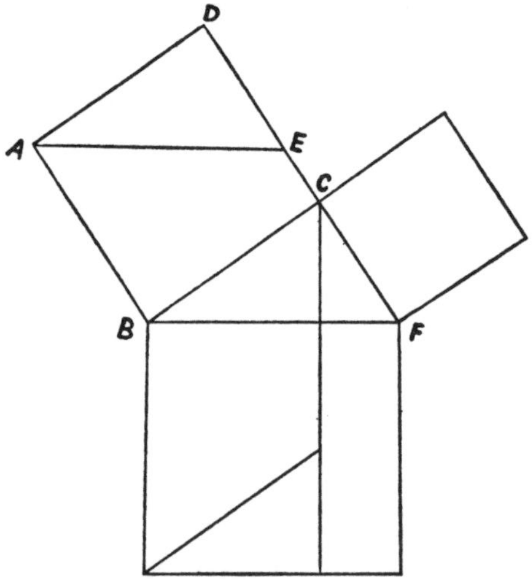

similarly the two parallelograms will be exactly the same size; in other words, they would cover each other. Accordingly, the area of a rectangle is the same as the square next to it."

"Now I know what it means to prove something," said Steven triumphantly.

The next day Steven went to George with a long face. "Imagine, I told my classmates that I could change a rectangle into a square of equal area and a square into a rectangle of equal area, naturally, first determining that one side . . ."

George was amazed. "How do you know all this?"

"I discovered it yesterday when you were proving the theorem to me.

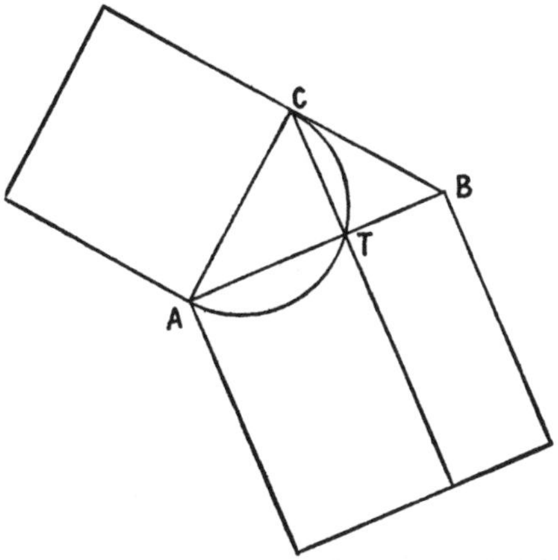

"The side of the square is a side of a right-angled triangle. I draw a semicircle on this side. The foot of the perpendicular (T) will lie on this circle, and AT will be an arc of this circle, forming a small triangle (ATC). Extending the line AT, the side of the triangle forms the larger triangle ABC. I draw a square on the side AB, which is divided into two rectangles, the left one of which is equal in area to the first square I drew. In the same way, I construct another square on the other side equal in area to the right-hand rectangle."

"Fine! That's all correct, so why do you have such a long face?"

"Because the boys won't believe that the square has the same area as the rectangle unless I can take the square into pieces, which, if put together in another way, will form the rectangle, and the other way around. Please help me with it, George!"

The two boys got together, worked, drew, and argued until the proof was ready.

Changing a Rectangle into a Square

We construct the square, which is equal in area to the rectangle. We measure off the length of its side from B on the longer side of the rectangle ABCD, and we get the point G. We measure off DG from A, and get the point H. Through this point, we draw a line

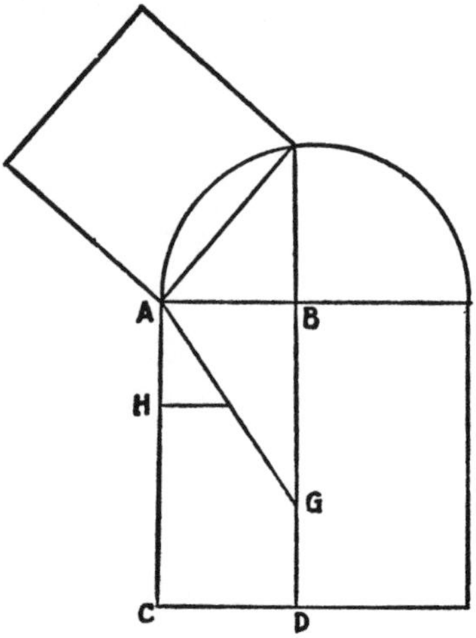

parallel to AB to AG. We cut along the line AG, and then we slide the triangle ABG till the point G is on the extension of CD. The little triangle cut off at the top just fills the space at the bottom.

Steve and George experimented to see if this would apply to all rectangles; and they found that it did so.

Changing a Square into a Rectangle

We want to change the square ABCD into a rectangle of the same area, one of the sides being DE.

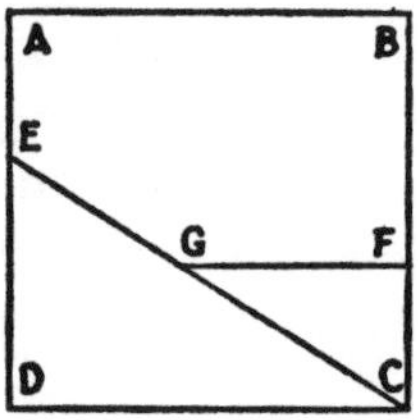

We measure off the length CF (CF = AE) and draw GF, which is parallel to AB. Now, if the square is drawn onto a piece of paper, we can cut the square along EC and FG, and so get three pieces. If we now place the upper part so that it touches GC, then the small triangle GFC will complete the rectangle. So we managed to complete the task by cutting the square into three pieces.

But is it possible to have any given side? After thinking about it, we can see that it is not quite so simple. If E is the midpoint of a side, then we need only to cut the square along the line running through the center, parallel to one of the sides, and place the two rectangles side by side.

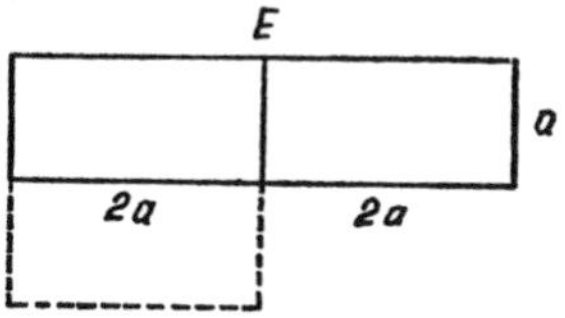

One of the sides of the rectangle formed in this way will be four times the length of the other, since one side is half the length of the side of the square and the other twice the length of the side of the square. If one of the sides of the rectangle is shorter than half the side of the square, we find that GF does not cut EC. In this case, cutting the square into only three pieces will not do.

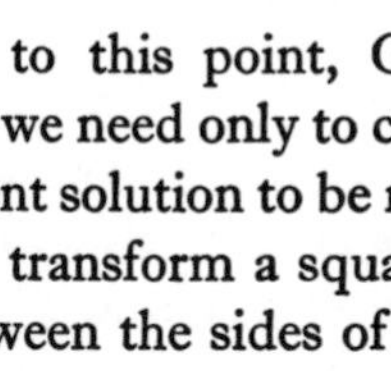

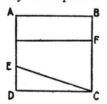

When the boys got to this point, George exclaimed: "It's interesting to notice that we need only to change one of the sides of the rectangle for a different solution to be required. We have found that it is not possible to transform a square into a rectangle with two cuts if the ratio between the sides of the rectangle is greater than one to four."

"Never mind; then we shall have to cut the square into more pieces," said Steven, who was anxious to find a general solution. "If we could change a one-to-four ratio rectangle into another with a larger ratio, the problem would be solved by taking an extra step."

After some thought they came up with a solution.

Changing a Rectangle into Another with Given Sides

They considered the previous diagram, which has one sloping cut, but not diagonally, and a small triangle. One side of the small triangle is equal to the length by which one of the sides of the new triangle is longer than that of the old one. They measured off this length (HC) along the longer side of the rectangle and drew a line through, parallel to the other side. The peak of the small triangle must lie on this line, but where? It must be at a point which, when connected to C and extended to the top left-hand corner, will form a similar small triangle.

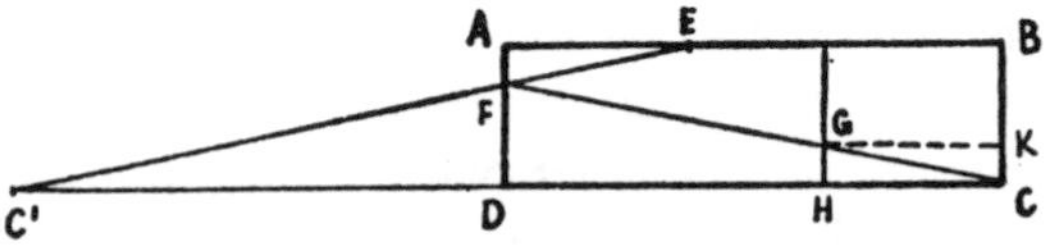

They got this point by producing CD to C′ where C′D = DC, and connecting C′ to E, where AE = HC. Then FC could be drawn giving the small triangle GHC. After cutting the rectangle, the trapezium on the right, ABCF, is moved down, and the small triangle GCK is fitted in.

Changing a Square into a Rectangle with a Ratio Greater Than One to Four

Following on from the above, this is done in two steps. First we cut the square along a line connecting the midpoint of two sides; we place the two halves side by side to form a one-to-four rectangle. Then we transform this into a rectangle which is longer than this in one dimension. Obviously we have to cut the original square into not three but five pieces.

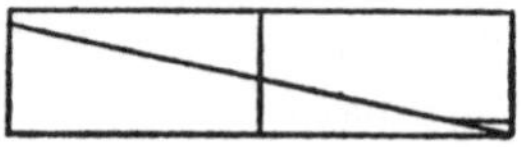

The boys thought this over: If the ratio of the sides is greater than one to four, then the square must be cut into three; when the ratio of the sides is exactly one to four, it is cut into two; and when it is smaller than one to four, it must be cut into five pieces to form the required rectangle.

A New Linoleum

The scout-hut floor needed new linoleum. Mr Peters, the Scoutmaster, measured the hall: 12×12 yards. The shop stocked only pieces 12×9 yards. A quick calculation showed $12 \times 12 = 144$ square yards and $16 \times 9 = 144$ square yards, so that was all right. But when they came to the point of cutting the rectangle to form a square, everyone was a bit nervous of making the first cut, in case they made a mistake. Mr Peters proposed the following solution:

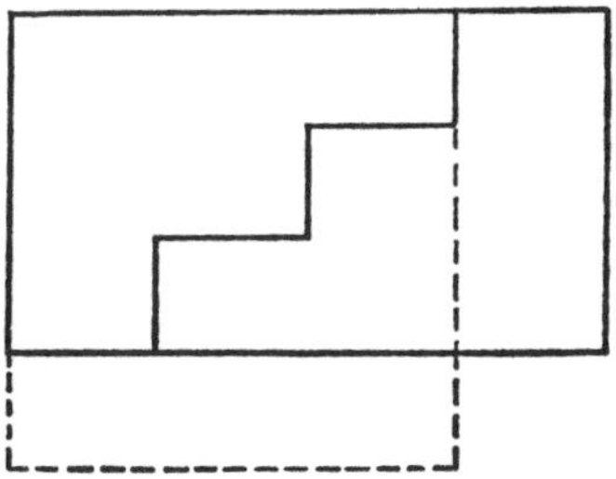

The linoleum is cut in "steps," where each "step" is 4 yards long and 3 yards wide. If the piece on the right is moved down one "step," a square will result – 12×12 yards.

Cutting Up and Making a Loss

When we transform a square into a rectangle or the other way around, the area remains unchanged. There are occasions when we change one shape into another and it appears that a part of the area is "lost." Reasoning tells us that this is impossible, yet when we come to it, it is not so easy to see where the "cheating" occurred. The most famous of these so-called "mathematical paradoxes" is connected with the chessboard.

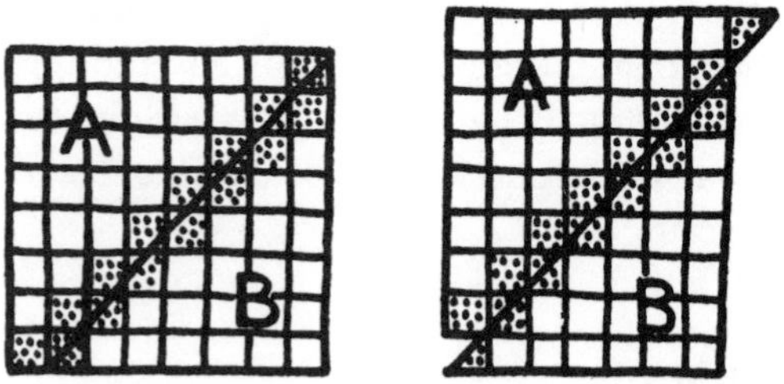

Draw an 8×8 square on a piece of paper and connect the second square from the bottom left-hand corner with the top right-hand one, as shown. Cut the square along the diagonal and move the left-hand side up one square, as shown. Now there will be a triangle missing at the bottom, and an extra triangle at the top. Cut the top triangle off and fit it into the missing space. This will then give us a rectangle with seven squares along one side and nine squares along the other, area 63, compared to the area of the original, which was 64. What happened to the missing square?

We know it did not disappear; we merely have to find it. Make another larger square using a fine pencil. Now, we can see that the line which forms the hypotenuse of the triangle at the top does not go through the corner of the square. The height of the triangle is not 1, but $1\frac{1}{7}$. All the triangles in the diagram are similarly shaped; their sides are in the ratio eight to seven, or $1\frac{1}{7}$. Therefore, when we fit the small triangle into the empty space, the length of one side is truly 7, but the length of the other side is $8 + 1\frac{1}{7} = 9\frac{1}{7}$. Therefore the area of the rectangle is $7 \times 9\frac{1}{7} = 64$.

When you show this to anyone, it is best when the small squares are not drawn in. It is even better when only the small squares along the diagonal are drawn. There are 15 of these to start with, and only 14 when we finish.

This is, of course, not quite true, since when we cut the square, we are not cutting along the true diagonal of the square, and there is a little bit left over in each case.

In this trick only the squares along the line take part; the others are merely accessories.

We have a similar paradox when we cut a 3×10-cm. rectangle into four pieces, as shown, and fit the pieces together.

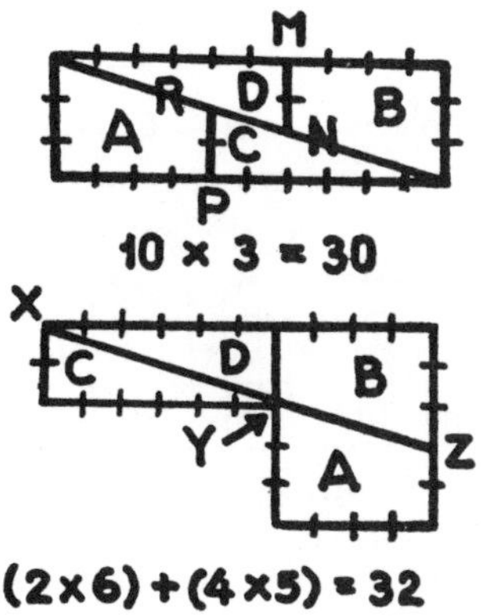

We get one rectangle area $2 \times 6 = 12$ square cm. and another 4×5 area, 20 square cm. The total is 32 square cm., and the area of the original is only 30 square cm. We appear to have gained 2 square cm. Where is the mistake? If we want to calculate the area of the various parts in the first diagram, we have to know the exact sizes of MN and PR. Using the idea of congruent triangles, we have $10{:}6 = 3{:}MN$, giving $MN = 1{\cdot}8$ cm., which is also the length of PR. Once we have found this, the paradox disappears, because the area of one of the triangles is $1{\cdot}8 \times 6 \div 2 = 5{\cdot}4$ square cm. and the area of one trapezium is $(3 + 1{\cdot}8) \times 4 \div 2 = 9{\cdot}6$ square cm.

The two together have an area of 15 square cm., and if we have two of each, the total area is 30 square cm.

If we have a careful look at the second diagram, the mistake becomes obvious here as well. The line XY is *not* a continuation of YZ, because they are only nearly at an angle of 180 degrees.

Another Chessboard

Divide the board into two rectangles. Then further divide the upper half into two triangles and the lower into two trapeziums.

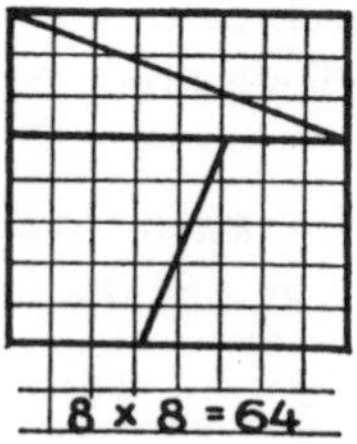

The area of the whole is 8 × 8 = 64 square cm. But if we put the pieces together in a different way, we get a rectangle 5 × 13 with area 65 square cm. We have "gained" 1 square cm.

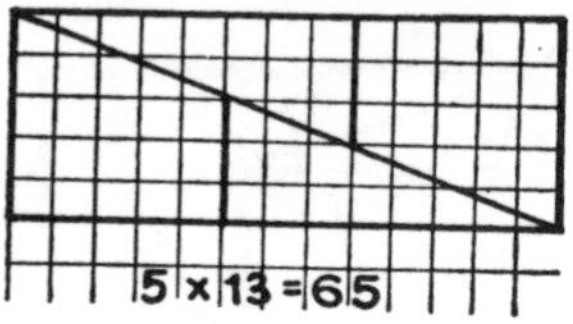

We have not really, of course. Along the "diagonal" of the rectangle there will be a series of little pieces which will come to 1 square cm. when added together.

If, on the other hand, we try to convert, in a similar fashion, a true 5 × 13 rectangle into an 8 × 8 square, the upper rectangle of the square will be a little too high and the lower one a little too wide.

We can fit the same shapes together so that their area comes to 63 square cm., giving us apparently another alternative.

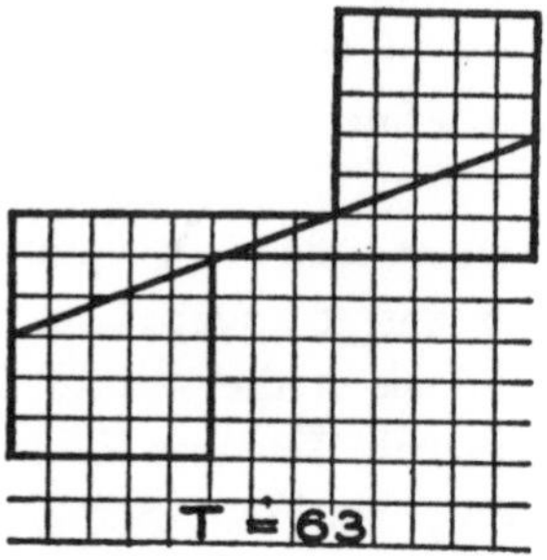

Examining this more carefully, we can see that the lower triangle has to be slid under the upper one, "losing" 1 square cm.

One would imagine that this sort of thing can be done with any square, not only an 8×8 chessboard. Yet this is not quite so. Have another look at the three diagrams. The area of the square is $5 \times 13 = 65$ square cm. Write the sides down in order of size: 5, 8, 13. Note that $5 + 8 = 13$. This series could be extended in both directions to give 1, 1, 2, 3, 5, 8, 13, 21, 34, 55.

Every number is the sum of the two preceding it. This sort of series is known as a Fibonacci series, and it also has the following interesting property: If any number in the series is multiplied by itself, the result is one more, or one less, than the product of its two neighbors.

For example:

$$2 \times 2 = 1 \times 3 + 1$$
$$3 \times 3 = 2 \times 5 - 1$$
$$5 \times 5 = 3 \times 8 + 1$$
$$8 \times 8 = 5 \times 13 - 1$$
$$13 \times 13 = 8 \times 21 + 1, \text{ etc.}$$

We must therefore choose the size of the square so that the length of its sides is one number from the Fibanocci series and the lengths of the sides of the rectangle are the two neighboring numbers. Then we shall "gain" or "lose" a unit.

Different and Yet the Same

Have a look at the two diagrams below. They are completely different, yet they have certain things in common. Both are so-

called "closed curves," and in neither case do the lines cross each other.

Therefore we should be able to alter one to the other. For example, a circle made out of string can be changed into the irregular shape and vice versa, without cutting or tying knots. While we are doing this, certain properties remain the same. We can use these for various interesting tricks, although their study is a branch of modern mathematics called topology.

Pick up a square handkerchief by opposite corners and turn it rapidly so that it forms a roll. With a rolled-up handkerchief we can do various tricks.

Knot the Handkerchief

Ask someone to pick up the handkerchief by its ends and tie a knot in it without letting go. This appears impossible, since a closed curve has no knot in it, and no matter how we change its shape, no knot will appear. If, however, you fold your arms before picking up the handkerchief, a knot will be in the handkerchief when you unfold your arms.

The point is that when you pick up the two ends of the handkerchief, your arms and the handkerchief will form a closed curve with a "knot" in your arms. When you unfold your arms, you are merely transferring the knot from one part of the closed curve to another.

There is a variation of this trick using a piece of string or a tie.

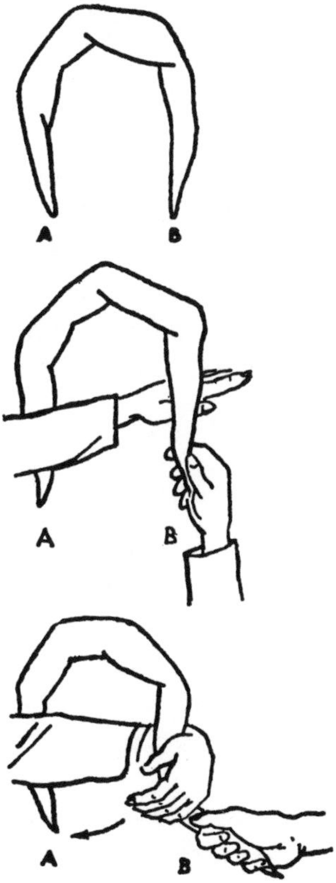

The string is placed on the table as shown. Pick up one end with your right hand and slide your left hand under it. Turn your hand palm upward quickly and pick up the other end. When you pull your hands apart, there will be a knot in the string. The quicker you move your hand, the more difficult it is to imitate the trick.

Freeing the Index Finger

Ask someone to extend his right hand and point with the index finger. Put the rolled-up handkerchief around it and cross the ends. Ask the person to place his left index finger over the tip of the right-hand one.

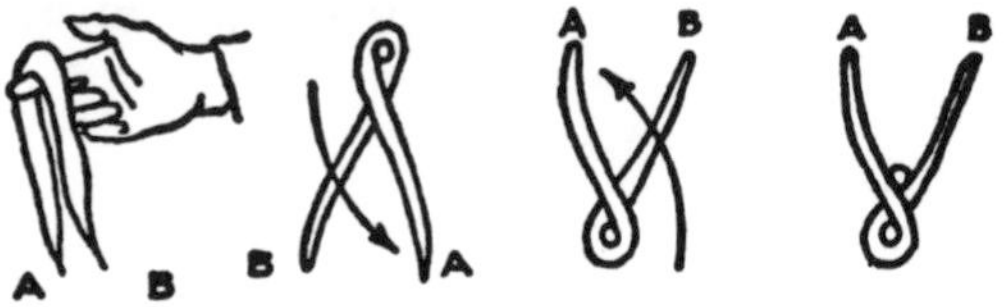

Then, as shown in the diagrams, knot the handkerchief over the two index fingers; fold it first downward and then up. It looks as if the fingers are completely trapped. Ask the person whose fingers you have trapped to pull out his upper finger. Then get hold of the other fingertip with one hand and pull both ends of the handkerchief together. The apparently safely secured knot becomes untied with one pull.

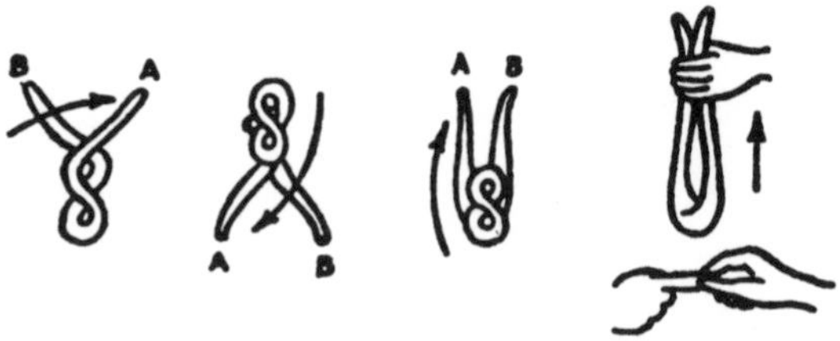

The secret of this is that the lower index finger remains outside the closed curve formed when you knot the two ends of the handkerchief.

The only thing to watch is that the end marked A is kept nearest to you. If you use a piece of string or a silk scarf, it is possible to make more turns, and so the trick becomes even more spectacular.

Inside or Outside?

Anybody can decide whether a point is inside or outside a closed curve. At least, that is what one thinks when considering a closed curve such as one formed by a piece of string whose ends are joined. However, there are other shapes that one can call "closed curves," and they are more complicated; these can be used for various tricks. The "magician" must merely know the shape he is "working" with. The few shapes can be easily remembered, and the tricks can be quite interesting. The simplest involves a piece of string doubled around its midpoint and arranged in a spiral.

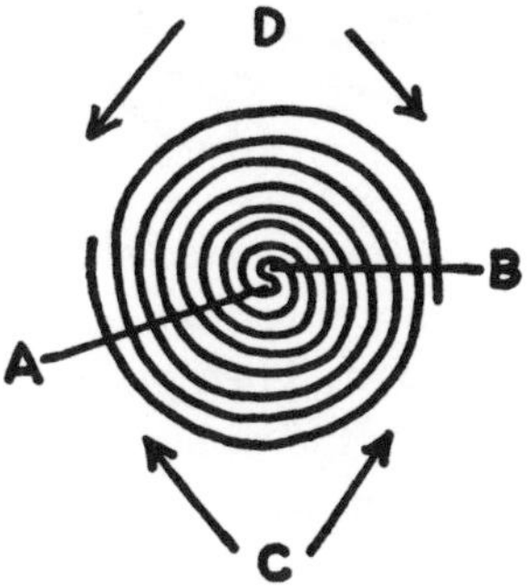

If the two ends are now joined, we shall have a closed curve. If you put your finger inside the closed curve and pull at the joined ends, the complete removal of the string will be prevented by your finger. If you put your finger outside the curve, then there is no reason why the string should not be removed completely. The trick consists of asking someone whether the point A is inside or outside the closed curve. If it is decided that it is outside, then ask him to hold the string at A and pull the two ends toward D, and he will be disappointed to find that it is inside. If he says that it is inside, then pull the ends toward C, and again he will be proved wrong. However, if, instead of A, we choose the curve B, then the roles of C and D are reversed.

The Giant's Garters

Think of one of those old-fashioned garters made of a piece of elastic, the two ends of which were sewn together. Tie together the two ends of a long piece of string – about ten yards in length; this will be the Giant's garter.

Ask someone to make a complicated shape on the floor with the string, the only condition being that no one part of the string should pass over another part. Then place newspapers all around, so that only a square part of the whole shows. Seeing only part of an irregular figure, it is even more difficult to decide whether a point is inside or outside the closed curve. If you know one important property of closed curves, then it is easy to make the correct decision. If you watch one point, which you know is inside the curve, as you put the newspaper down, then the rest is easy. Such a point could be the one marked A.

Closed curves have a famous, apparently very simple property. If two points inside the curve are connected by a continuous line, then the original curve is either not cut at all or it is cut 2, 4, 6, 8 (that is, an even number of) times. This is obvious, since if we go outside the closed curve to end up inside it, we must re-enter it. The number of times the line crosses the curve must therefore be even. If the line connects a point inside the curve with one outside it, then the number of times the line crosses the curve must be 3, 5, 7. That is an odd number.

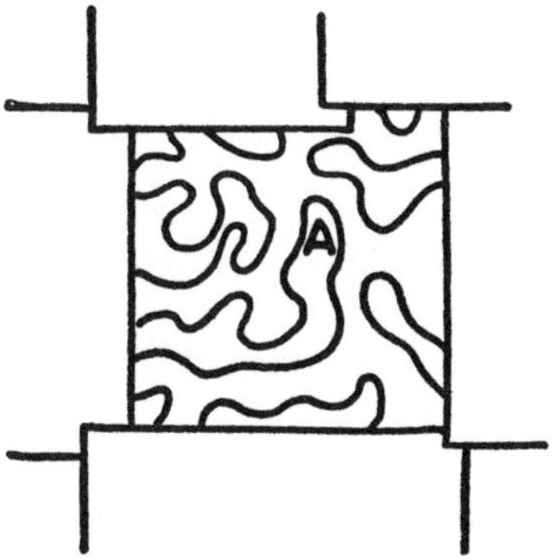

If, therefore, we have noted a point inside the curve, then we can connect this point to any other point by an imaginary line. By counting the number of times the line crosses the curve, we can determine whether a given point is inside or outside the curve. The proof of a point's being inside the curve is demonstrated by pulling the string with a finger on the given point. It will not be possible to remove your finger.

A variation of this game is to stick a number of pins into the figure, apparently at random. If they are all at points outside the curve, it will still be possible to remove the string. Yet another variation is to ask someone to draw a complicated closed curve on a piece of paper. Fold part of it behind and ask that a number of points be put on the paper. Then you can quickly show which points are inside and which are outside the closed curve.

String Bracelets

The previous tricks were all based on the properties of closed curves. But sometimes it is not easy to decide when a point is inside or outside the curve. This may be difficult to believe, but it is so, and some tricks are based on this fact.

Tie a piece of string around your wrists as shown:

Tell your audience that you will tie a knot in the string without untying the string from your wrists. Make a loop in the string, pull it *under* the "bracelet" on one of your wrists, twist it once, then pull it *over* the same hand, then under the "bracelet," and finally over your hand again. Pull your hands apart, and there will be a knot in the string.

How can we make a knot in a closed curve which did not contain a knot already?

When you have a good look, you can see that your body, arms, and the string do not form a closed curve, since there is a gap between the string and your wrists. Through this gap the loop can be drawn, making the knot possible.

Obviously you should have a bit of practice first, as a trick like this is effective only if it is done quickly and cleanly.

It is simpler to put a rubber band on the apparently closed curve that is formed by your body, arms, and the string. Put the band over your hand and pull it through your "bracelet." Then pull the upper part over your hand, and the rubber band will be on the string. It can be removed by following these steps in reverse.

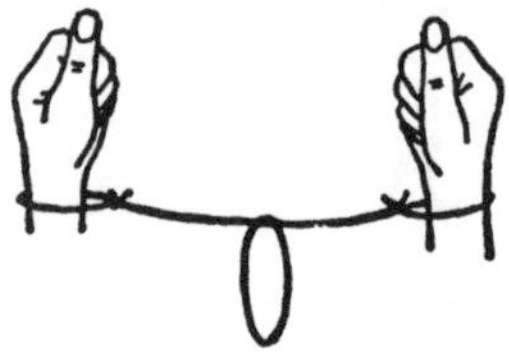

We can involve more people by tying pieces of string between the wrists of two people. To start with, the two pieces of string should be separate and should not cross.

Make a loop with one piece of string and draw it through the "bracelet" around the other person's wrist. Put the loop over that person's hand, and the two people will be tied together. Of course, they can be separated in this way as well.

If a few couples are tied together like this, it is quite funny to watch them trying to free themselves. They will twist their arms and bodies, all to no avail. The "conjurer" will, however, be able to effect their freedom.

Magical Knots

There are some complicated-looking knots which are not knots at all. One of these is shown in the diagram.

Make the knot on the left first, then from this make the one on the right. When you pull the two ends, the whole thing will come undone.

Tricks with a Vest

Since vests have become fashionable again, it is not difficult to find someone wearing one. A vest, from a topological point of view, is a peculiar plane: when buttoned, the vest or sleeveless pullover is a two-sided plane with four separate edges (the two armholes, the opening for the neck, and the lower edge). The unbuttoned vest has also two surfaces but three edges – the two armholes and the neck and lower edge connected. Using these facts, we can show you one or two tricks.

Ask someone who is wearing a vest to remove his jacket. Put a loop of string around his right arm and put his right thumb into the right-hand pocket of the vest.

Ask another person to remove the string, without the person wearing the string removing his thumb from his pocket. He will try to pull the string over the person's head and shoulders, but it will not work. Then you offer to try. Pull the string through the armhole and over the person's head; then pull the string through the left armhole and put his left arm through it. Now the string will be around the person's chest, and you merely have to drop it to the ground for him to step through.

After you have succeeded with this trick, you can try a more complicated one. For example, ask the person wearing the vest to clasp his hands in front of him, and tell him that you will turn his vest inside out without his hands being unclasped. Unbutton the vest, lift it up over his head, turn it inside out through the arm-holes, then put it back.

If this can be done without the vest's being unbuttoned, it can also be done with a sleeveless pullover. Indeed, a loose pullover might be better than a tight vest. The trick can be done in the same manner, and it can be made more effective if you do it with the pullover you are wearing, with your hands tied together. So that you can work with your hands, leave about two or three feet of string between your wrists.

You can also show your friends that you can turn your pullover inside out, with your hands tied while you are wearing your jacket. Pull the jacket over your head at the shoulders and then turn your pullover inside out as we showed you above. Remember that these tricks are no good for your clothes, so do not do them when you are wearing your best suit.

The most impressive trick of this type is the one in which you remove someone's vest without his taking his jacket off!

Unbutton the vest and pull the left-hand side of the jacket through the left armhole from the outside. Then turn this armhole around to the right side and pull the right-hand side of the jacket through. While you are doing this, the left armhole crosses the wearer's chest from left to right. When the vest is hanging from the right shoulder under the jacket, push the right sleeve under it up to the elbow, then fold the sleeve and pull the vest through.

Tricks with Rubber Bands

Here we can use the elastic properties of rubber.

Put your index finger into a rubber band. Then put the band under your middle finger and put this finger through as well, as

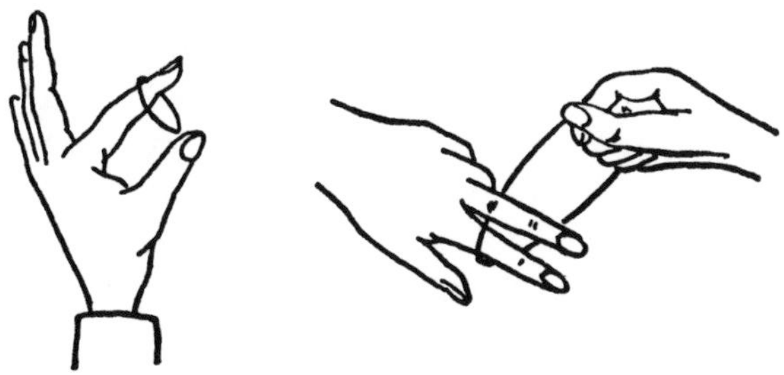

shown. While you are doing this, keep your fingers straight. Now ask someone to get hold of your index finger. If you now bend your middle finger, this will free the index finger, although previously the rubber band was tight around both fingers.

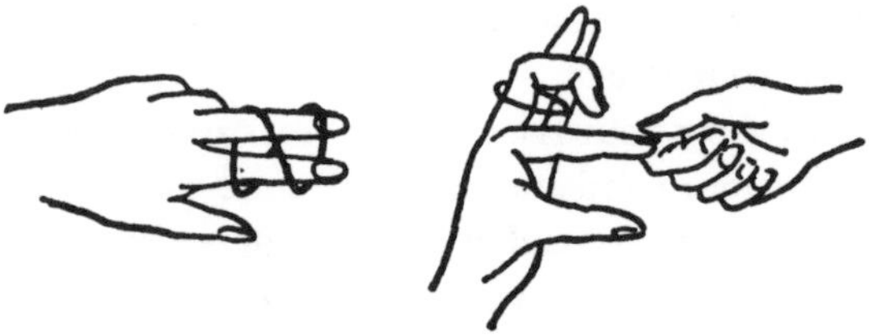

For the next trick you need a broader band. Hold it as shown in the drawing; then, by moving your fingers, put two twists in the rubber band. We have not reached the trick yet! The rubber band will easily return to its previous position if you let it go.

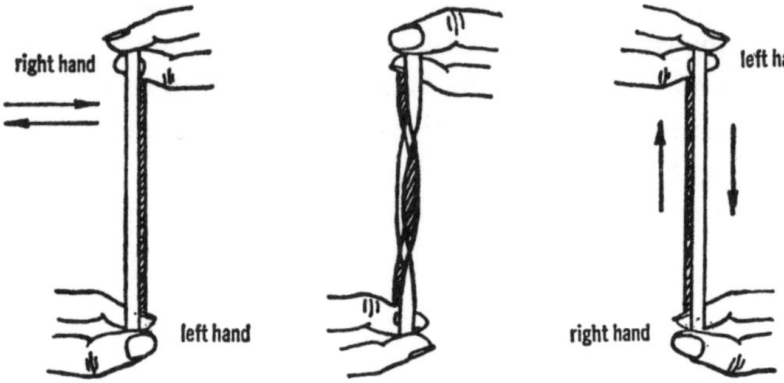

Now ask someone to stand opposite you and take over the band by holding it with his right index finger and thumb on top and his left finger and thumb below. Now ask him to remove the twists from the rubber band, without letting go, but by merely moving the fingers. Whatever he tries, nothing will work. When you take it back again, you will be able to do it quite easily. Why are you able to do something easily that the other person could not do at all? Because the twisted band, your body, arms, and fingers form a cycle where this is possible. But when the other person takes it over, the problem is different. What was a right-to-left twist to you is a left-to-right twist to the other person, so it is impossible for him to do the same as you.

CHAPTER 10

WRITING IN CODE

There are not many people who have not at some time wished to find a way of writing in a code that nobody but themselves could understand. We know that there are several ways of attempting this, since many state secrets are passed on by these means. The decoding of secret writings is almost a science; there are skilled people who are specialists in this field. The simplest codes are based on swapping letters: a certain letter in the alphabet is always replaced by another letter or sign. This system can be made more complex, but those skilled at solving codes can soon crack it. They usually start from the letter which occurs most often, being represented by always the same letter. It is known that in French, English, Hungarian, and German the letter *e* occurs most often; in Spanish *o*; in Italian *e* and *i*; and in Russian *a*. Starting from this, the experts can soon turn the text in code into an understandable message.

Much more difficult to solve is a code which needs a special "key." During World War II the following method was used. The people writing to each other each possessed identical copies of a book. Each letter was shown as a fraction, giving the page number and the number of the letter on that page. For example, $\frac{125}{12}$ meant the 12th letter on page 125. This method has the advantage that the same letter can be shown over and over again, using different numbers each time, and those who do not have the book in question can never decode the message. This type of code requires that the secret is kept perfectly and that the book, which is the key to the whole thing, is never allowed to fall into the wrong hands.

A Grid Code

An interesting method is described in one of Jules Verne's books. The code was constructed with the help of a grid. In this system every letter is represented by itself (that is, the *p* means the letter *p*), but the letters are written into the squares of a grid and the letters appearing in the empty squares of the grid are placed in a definite order. The grid can be placed on the text in different ways, and the code can be broken only if the grid and message are lost or stolen.

In Verne's book some bandits managed to acquire not only a secret telegram but also the grid, and so they could read the code. This is how Verne describes it: The grid is a square of cardboard, each side 6 cm. long. It is divided into 36 smaller squares, each approximately 1 square cm. Among the 36 squares, 27 are "full" and 9 are "empty." In other words, there are nine square holes among the 36.

One of the bandits copies the grid and notes that one of the squares has a small inked cross on it. The telegram has 36 letters, and the letters are written down in the form of a square. The grid is then put on the square, and they start trying to solve the puzzle. They at once discover that they must copy the letters appearing through the empty holes, because the grid must be turned in four different directions in order that all the letters can be read.

We can try this quite simply if we make a grid and place it on a blank piece of paper. We then write the numbers 1 to 9 in the empty squares, and if we then make a quarter turn and write 10 to 18, turn again a quarter and write 19 to 27, and finally turn a quarter and write 28 to 36, we shall have all the numbers from 1 to 36 written in a square when the grid is lifted. Instead of these numbers we can write letters, so that the first letter replaces the figure 1, the second the figure 2 and so on.

Let's try this method of writing in code. As an example, we'll take the first two lines of a nursery rhyme:

There was a little girl
Who had a little curl

Arrange the letters in a grid of 36 squares. Cut out two squares of the same size; one will be the grid and the other will contain the message. By turning the grid three times, all the 36 letters must appear once, and once only. The number of "windows" in the grid must be a quarter of the total number of letters in the square – in our case, $36 \div 4 = 9$. Let's mark which is the top of the square.

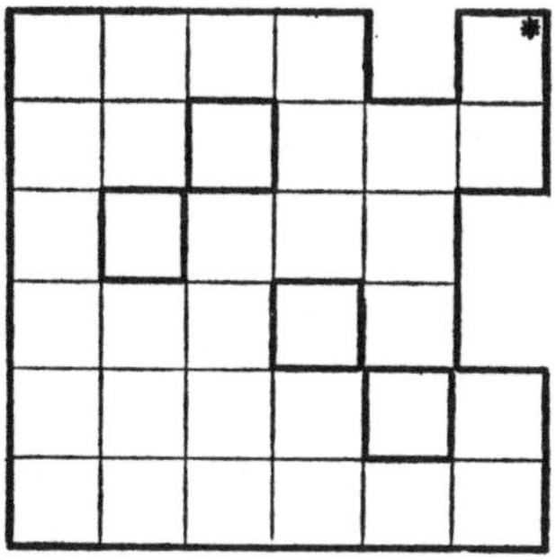

The first hole can be anywhere. In our diagram we chose the fifth square of the first row. We cut out this hole, put the grid over the other square, and mark this position, this being the position of the first letter. Move the square a quarter turn three times and mark where the window comes, because we can have no more windows in these positions. Whenever we cut a new window, we must check the position in the same way. It helps if we write numbers in the windows before putting in the letters.

In our diagram we cut windows in the fifth square of the first row, the third square of the second row, the second and sixth squares of the third row, the fourth and sixth squares of the fourth row, the first and fifth squares of the fifth row, and the first square of the sixth row. The grid was turned clockwise.

The numbers and letters are then arranged like this:

18	16	31	33	1	27	R	G	L	C	T	L
28	26	2	12	35	25	I	A	H	T	R	D
24	3	23	32	11	4	A	E	H	E	I	R
22	29	14	5	21	6	O	T	L	E	H	W
7	17	30	20	8	10	A	I	T	W	S	L
9	19	15	13	34	36	A	L	E	T	C	L

Such codes can be made by anyone. The size of the grid can be changed to fit the message. In Jules Verne's book, the grid was always sent by post. This risk that someone else would find the grid and the message and thereby be able to decode it could have been avoided by using binary numbers. In this way, the grid can be prepared by knowing just a few numbers.

There are two sorts of squares in the grid, those which have been cut out and those which have not. If we represent those which have been cut out as 1 and those which have not by 0, then we can write down our grid as:

0	0	0	0	1	0
0	0	1	0	0	0
0	1	0	0	0	1
0	0	0	1	0	1
1	0	0	0	1	0
1	0	0	0	0	0

Everybody can recognize the above as a set of binary numbers, which can be translated into the decimal system. The first row gives 10, which represents 2 in the decimal system. The second row gives 1,000 in the binary system, or 8 in the decimal system. The third row gives 10,001, that is, 17 in the decimal system; the fourth 101, or 5; the fifth 100,010, or 34; and the sixth 100,000 or 32.

Therefore, a telegram including the numbers 2, 8, 17, 5, 34, and 32 for conversion into binary numbers would have given the key.

Numbers Instead of Letters

The Greeks used several kinds of codes. One of the simplest involves replacing letters by numbers. The letters are arranged as follows:

	1	2	3	4	5
1	—	f	k	p	u
2	a	—	l	q	v
3	b	g	—	r	w
4	c	h	m	—	x
5	d	i	n	s	y
6	e	j	o	t	z

Every letter is given two numbers, one signifying the row it is in, the other the column. Putting the number for the row first, the letter l becomes 23, v becomes 25, and so on.

We could then write: 52/21–43/32–63–52–53–32/63–53/42–63–23–52–51–21–55. (I am going on holiday.)

Even this is difficult to solve. It makes it even more difficult if we do not write down the words separately, but put the gaps in at random. The person for whom the message is intended will understand it anyway, and for anyone else the problem of deciphering it becomes more difficult. For example, the message above could be written as: 52–21–43–32–63/52–53–32–63–53–42–63/23/52–51–21–55.

Signs Instead of Letters

Another simple and easily remembered code is to write a simple sign for each individual letter, writing down the alphabet as:

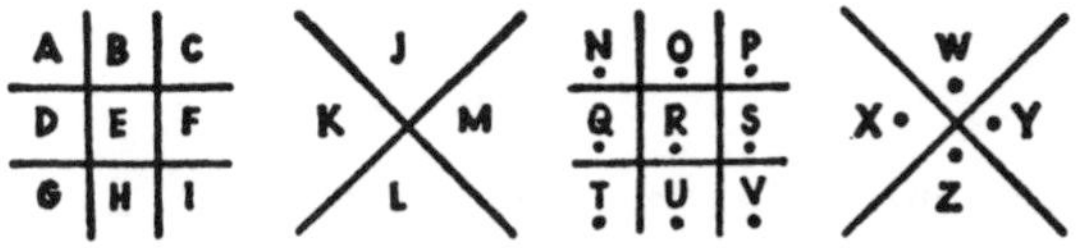

We put the part of the diagram occupied by the letter we want. For instance, instead of F we write ⊏, instead of H ⊓, in place of N •⌋, for M <, for W V̇.

We can use these for words like these:  (answer); or  (imagination).

Rearranged Letters

A common form of code uses letters that are not changed to represent anything else, but their order is changed.

The letters are placed in some order that is known only by the two people concerned. Let us take a simple example, the name

Elizabeth Carpenter (consisting of 18 letters). Let us write it down in this form:

E	C
L	A
I	R
Z	P
A	E
B	N
E	T
T	E
H	R

The correct message is obtained by reading from top to bottom. However, if we read them from left to right and arrange them in random words, then we could get: ECLA IRZ PAEBN ETTEHR.

A skillful person could soon decipher this, of course. His task would be more difficult if we wrote the same thing like this:

E	Z	E	C	P	T
L	A	T	A	E	E
I	B	H	R	N	R

And then the coded message could read: EZEC PTLAT AEEIBH RNR.

In the above example we arranged the letters in a 6 × 3 shape. We can, of course, use other arrangements. Let us have a look at a message sent by a spy: "Enemy attack tomorrow." This has nineteen letters. Arranging this in a 5 × 4 (=20) rectangle, we put a so-called "blind" letter in the last square, like this:

E	Y	A	O	R
N	A	C	M	O
E	T	K	O	W
M	T	T	R	X

Then we rewrite the message as: EYA ORNA CMO ETK OWMTTRX.

This type of code can be made even more difficult in several ways. We shall show you two of them:

1. Agree with your partner on a well-known date (well known so that it is easily remembered, preferably one in which all the digits are different).

As an example, let us take 1945 (the end of World War II). Write down the letters of the previous example in four columns of five letters each. Number the columns and write down our key number underneath, thus:

1	2	3	4
1	9	4	5
E	A	K	R
N	T	T	R
E	T	O	O
M	A	M	W
Y	C	O	X

The natural order of the numbers in 1945 is 1, 4, 5, 9. Rearrange the columns thus:

1	4	5	9
E	K	R	A
N	T	R	T
E	O	O	T
M	M	W	A
Y	O	X	C

Then we can rearrange the horizontal rows as: EKR ANTRTE OOT MMWAY OXC.

The person who wants to decode the message knows, of course, how to rearrange the letters in their five rows.

2. For the coding of longer messages, this method is of no use. Here we must have a key word instead of a number. The key word should preferably contain letters that are all different. For instance, let us take the ten-letter noun: milkchurns.

No two letters are the same. Write it down and number the letters:

1	2	3	4	5	6	7	8	9	10
m	i	l	k	c	h	u	r	n	s

Now arrange the letters alphabetically and write down the numbers belonging to the letters underneath:

c	h	i	k	l	m	n	r	s	u
5	6	2	4	3	1	9	8	10	7

This, then, is the key number. If we want to transmit the following fifty-letter message: "Enemy attack tomorrow; expect strongest fire from the north."

Then, as before, we write down the message in ten rows of five letters:

1	2	3	4	5	6	7	8	9	10
E	A	K	R	X	S	G	I	O	N
N	T	T	R	P	T	E	R	M	O
E	T	O	O	E	R	S	E	T	R
M	A	M	W	C	O	T	F	H	T
Y	C	O	E	T	N	F	R	E	H

Rearrange the columns according to the order of our key word:

5	6	2	4	3	1	9	8	10	7
X	S	A	R	K	E	O	I	N	G
P	T	T	R	T	N	M	R	O	E
E	R	T	O	O	E	T	E	R	S
C	O	A	W	M	M	H	F	T	T
T	N	C	E	O	Y	E	R	H	F

Write the message in random words: XS ARKEO INGPT TRTNMROEER TOOE TERSC OAWMMHF TTT NCEOY ERHF.

The person who receives the message knows that the letters must be arranged in ten columns and five rows. He also knows the key word and therefore the key number and arranges the letters accordingly.

The letters remain – the number changes.

We have already seen that every letter can be quite easily expressed as a two-figure number. The advantage of this method is that it is quite easy to remember, but the disadvantage is that this type of code is relatively easy to break.

It is possible to make this method more complicated, so that the task facing anyone trying to break the code would be very much more difficult.

Write the alphabet in three rows and ten columns (we include some blanks to make the number up to 30):

			1	2	3	4	5	6	7	8	9	10
9	6	3	—	a	b	c	d	e	f	g	h	i
8	5	2	j	—	k	l	m	n	o	p	q	r
7	4	1	—	s	t	u	v	w	x	y	z	—

On the left-hand side there are three numbers, instead of one, as used previously. Now each letter could be written as any of three two-figure numbers. For example, 96, 66, and 36 all mean *e*. If we write the word "telephone" as 73–36–54–66–58–69–57–26–96, the letter *e* was written three different ways.

Letters Instead of Numbers

We have seen a way of putting things into a code in which numbers replace letters. Now we will do it the other way around and replace numbers by letters.

Every letter will represent one single number, and each letter will represent a different number.

We shall be showing you problems in which unknown numbers will be represented not by numbers but by dots. Numbers can be written later instead of these dots.

To solve these problems beyond getting the basic idea needs no special mathematical knowledge, merely common sense.

In these problems it is best to treat the numbers 0 and 1 the same way, because numbers do not usually start with a 0; all numbers, when multiplied by 0, give 0; and when a number is multiplied by 1, the number remains unchanged. If we add one number to another and the result is the same as one of the numbers, then the other number must have been 0, etc. When multiplying, 5 is also easy to recognize, since an odd number will give a number that ends in 5, an even number a result that ends with a 0. If we start working in this way, we shall soon find out some of the numbers that we can substitute for the letters.

Let us start. First a simple addition:

$$\begin{array}{r} \text{BDCE} \\ +\text{BDAE} \\ \hline \text{AECBE} \end{array}$$

We can see two things straight away: two four-figure numbers added together must give a result below 20,000; therefore, A = 1; also, since E + E = E, E must be 0.

Since the first column gives no remainder, C + A = B, or B = C + 1, because we have already found that A = 1. Therefore, the sum of the two numbers must start with 10 (A = 1, E = 0); so, then, B must be 5. But B = C + 1; therefore, C = 4 and D = 2. The whole sum must be:

$$\begin{array}{r} 5240 \\ +5210 \\ \hline 10{,}450 \end{array}$$

In the next problem we shall make an extra condition to make the solution easier.

The problem is:

$$\begin{array}{r} \text{DPJ} \\ \text{NDREE} \\ +\text{SEND} \\ \hline \text{CHEER} \end{array}$$

We are told that $E^2 = H$. Then H must be 4 or 9, because these are the only two squares having a single digit.

Suppose that H = 9. In the column where the thousands occur, there must be a remainder of 1; otherwise, N and C would not be different. Therefore, D + S = 19, which is impossible, because even if in the hundreds column there were a remainder of 2, D + S could not be greater than 7 + 8 = 15, which, with a remainder of 2, would come to 17. Then H would be 7, whereas we supposed that H = 9. Therefore, H must be 4, and E must be 2.

$$\begin{array}{r} DPJ \\ NDR22 \\ +S2ND \\ \hline C422R \end{array}$$

D + S + remainder = 14; therefore, D + S = 13. This can happen if: D = 8 and S = 5; D = 5 and S = 8; D = 7 and S = 6; D = 6 and S = 7. 4 + 9 cannot be used, since 4 is already taken by H.

If D = 8, then from the units column we get J = R, which is impossible. If D were to be 5, then the hundreds column would be 5 + R + 2 + remainder = 12, or 22. 2 cannot be the remainder of either the hundreds or the tens column, since out of the three numbers one is 2 and the other two no greater than 9 + 8 = 17. The remainder, therefore, must be 1; in other words, 5 + R + 2 + 1 = 12 (R = 4 is impossible, since H = 4).

If, then, D = 7, then 7 + R + 2 + 1 = 12. Then R = 2, which is also impossible, since E = 2. Therefore D can be only 2 and S = 7.

$$\begin{array}{r} 6PJ \\ N6R22 \\ +72N6 \\ \hline C422R \end{array}$$

From the hundreds column we get 6 + R + 2 + 1 (remainder) = 12, or R = 3.

$$\begin{array}{r} 6PJ \\ N6322 \\ +72N6 \\ \hline C4223 \end{array}$$

We can see from the units column that J = 5.

$$\begin{array}{r} 6P5 \\ N6322 \\ +72N6 \\ \hline C4223 \end{array}$$

The units now give 5 + 2 + 6 + 13, remainder 1.

The tens give $P + 2 + N + 1$ (remainder) $= 12$, or $P + N = 9$. Let us try this in the following cases:

P	N	
0	9	N cannot be nine, because C, which is 1 bigger, would not then be a single-digit number.
1	8	
2	7	impossible, because E = 2
3	6	impossible, because D = 6
4	5	impossible, because J = 5 and H = 4
5	4	impossible, as above
6	3	impossible, because D = 6
7	2	impossible, because E = 2
8	1	
9	0	impossible, because if N = 0, then the second number cannot be a five-figure, but only a four-figure number

Therefore, P = 1 and N = 8, or P = 8 and N = 1. N cannot be 1, because C, which is bigger by 1, would be 2, but E = 2. Therefore, only one possibility now remains, P = 1 and N = 8, C = 9. The solution is:

```
   615
 86322
 +7286
 ------
94,223
```

Let us have a look at a problem in which some of the numbers are replaced by *x*.

```
      x7x
   ______
xx)xxxxx
   x77
   ---
    x7x
    x7x
    ---
      xx
      xx
      --
```

Here we start by saying that the first digit of the result multiplied by xx gives $x77$. Among the numbers x, there cannot be another 7. One-figure numbers that when multiplied give a result which end in a 7 are 3 and 9. The first digit of the result must, therefore, be 3 or 9, and the divisor units must be either 9 or 3. If we suppose that the divisor takes the form $x9$ and we multiply it by 3, then 59 is the only number which will give a number like $x77$. In the other case, when the divisor is of the type $x3$ and we multiply by 9, then only 53 will give a number like $x77$. If in the first case we take the divisor to be 59 and we multiply by the divisor's second digit, 7, we get 413; we do not get a second line with 7 as the middle digit. It follows, then, that the divisor must be 53, the first digit of the result being 9. The last digit of the result, however, can only be a 1, because only by multiplying by 1 do we get a two-digit result (53 × 2 gives a three-figure number). The result is, therefore, 971. Multiplying this by 53, we get the number to be divided as 51,463, and the problem is solved:

```
      971
   ______
53)51463
   477
   ---
    376
    371
    ---
      53
      53
      --
```

Finally we shall show you a problem in which the numbers are replaced by letters and dots, all mixed up:

```
      A B C · B A C
      -----
      . . . .
      . . . .
      . . A
  . . . B
  -------------
    . . . . . .
```

We can see that among A, B, and C, A is the smallest number, because ABC × A gives a three-figure number and the other two lines are four-figure numbers.

Only 1, 2, and 3 are possible, because if a three-figure number in which the first digit is 4 is multiplied by 4, we will have a four-figure number.

A cannot be 1, because then from ABC × A, A × C = A. Similarly, if A = 3, then C = 1, which is impossible, because C must be larger than A. Therefore, A = 2. C must be a number which, when multiplied by 2, gives a result which ends in 2; therefore, C = 6. Writing the known numbers in, we get:

```
      2 B 6 · B 2 6
      -----
    . . . 6
      . . 2
  . . . B
  -----------
  . . . . . 6
```

From the third line of the multiplication, we see that 6 × B gives a two-figure number ending in B. We can write this as $10x + B$.

$$6B = 10x + B$$
$$5B = 10x$$
$$B = 2x$$

B must be an even number, that is, 4 or 8.

If B = 4, then the number to be multiplied must be 246. But multiplying this by B (that is, by 4) we get a three-figure number. Therefore, B = 8, and the solution is:

```
   286·826
   ----
  1716
   572
 2288
 ------
 236236
```

CHAPTER 11

MAGICAL SQUARES

If we were to say, "Draw a square, divide it into sixteen smaller squares, and put numbers into each square so that the sum of each vertical, horizontal, and diagonal line is the same," we would be faced with an interesting or a boring job, according to our individual taste.

There was a time when people supposed that numbers had magical powers, and some people used to wear numbers around their necks on a chain. It was during this time that these squares acquired the "magical" description. The name remained, although people's faith in magic declined as time passed. The problem also remains, and it is interesting and worth examining.

The magical square has Indian origins, and like so many other things in mathematics, came to Europe via the Arabs. There is evidence that such squares were constructed in the fourteenth century. To show you how much this problem used to interest people, even the German painter Dürer shows one of these squares in his etching *Melancholy:*

16	3	2	13
5	10	11	8
9	6	7	12
4	15	14	1

This square has a number of interesting things about it. The two middle numbers in the bottom line – 15 and 14 – read together give the year in which Dürer made the etching, 1514.

Not only does the sum of each row, column, and diagonal line come to the same, but the numbers in the four corners of the square (16, 13, 4, 1) and the four numbers in the middle (10, 11, 6, 7) each total 34.

The simplest square of this sort consists of 9 small squares. The problem is to write the numbers from 1 to 9 in such a way that the sum of each column, row, and diagonal comes to the same.

If we add all the numbers 1–9 together, we get 45. Obviously the sum of every line must come to 15. Taking three numbers so that they add up to 15, we get:

$1 + 5 + 9 = 15$
$1 + 6 + 8 = 15$
$2 + 4 + 9 = 15$
$2 + 5 + 8 = 15$
$3 + 4 + 8 = 15$
$3 + 5 + 7 = 15$
$4 + 5 + 6 = 15$

2	9	4
7	5	3
6	1	8

The number in the center is used on four occasions, when we add the second column and the second row and also when adding the numbers in the two diagonals. Therefore, we must use a number which occurs four times in the table above. Such a number is 5. The numbers in the four corners must occur three times; these are 2, 4, 6, and 8. The number of solutions varies according to the number of ways the numbers in the four corners can be arranged.

We can write any of the four numbers in the upper left-hand corner (representing four possible solutions). In the lower right-hand corner we can write only one number. The other two numbers can be placed two ways in the remaining corners. Altogether, then, there are $4 \times 2 = 8$ possible solutions. These are:

2	9	4
7	5	3
6	1	8

2	7	6
9	5	1
4	3	8

4	9	2
3	5	7
8	1	6

4	3	8
9	5	1
2	7	6

6	7	2
1	5	9
8	3	4

6	1	8
7	5	3
2	9	4

8	3	4
1	5	9
6	7	2

8	1	6
3	5	7
4	9	2

The square with nine numbers then can be filled relatively easily. Similarly, we can construct a square of a "higher order."

Fill in the Squares

Let us have a look at how we can construct a magic figure with 7 × 7 (49) squares.

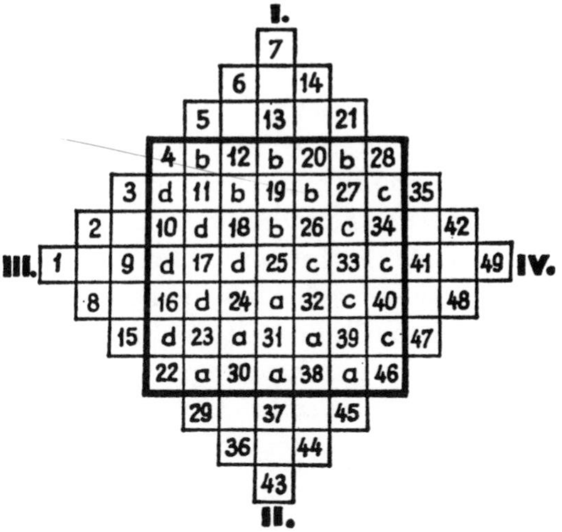

The diagram shows the method of construction. In the middle is the 7 × 7 square, outlined with a thick black line. The small squares outside are there merely to help us.

We shall start with the small square on the extreme left; let us write a 1 in it. Then, moving diagonally upward, write down all the numbers in order (4 will occupy the top left of the magical square) till we have 7 in the last square. Continue, starting with 8 from the square diagonally from 1. This way 49 will be in the square on the extreme right-hand edge of the diagram. If we do this, some of the places within the square will remain empty; moreover, the number of empty squares within the main square will equal the number of small squares outside it. Write the numbers outside into the corresponding squares inside, mirror fashion; in other words, the numbers in section I go into the squares marked with an *a*, the numbers in II into *b*, those in III into *c*, and those in IV into *d*, which will give:

4	29	12	37	20	45	28
35	11	36	19	44	27	3
10	42	18	43	26	2	34
41	17	49	25	1	33	9
16	48	24	7	32	8	40
47	23	6	31	14	39	15
22	5	30	13	38	21	46

We shall have our magical square, with every row, column, and diagonal adding to 175.

The square can be easily remembered. The first row starts with 4, and we write figures larger by 8 into every second square (4, 12, 20, 28). We start the second row diagonally under 12 with a number that is one less, that is, 11, and we again write into every second square a number that is 8 larger (11, 19, 27). Then diagonally under 11 the number ten with the corresponding 8-larger numbers (18, 26, 37), and so on.

Dealing with the remaining squares: we have 29 next to 4; then, similarly, in that row 37 and 45. Diagonally under 37 we have 36; continuing that row, we have 44; diagonally under 44 we have 43. Diagonally under 42 we have 41, then 49. $49 + 8 = 57$, but this is too big, so here we put 1, then 9, and so on.

With a little practice we can easily amaze those to whom this is shown, because those not in the know will find it difficult to guess the answer.

Move the Disks

The diagram below contains all the numbers from 1 to 25. All the columns, rows, and diagonals add up to 65. Besides these usual ones, 65 will also be obtained if we add the numbers along the so-called "broken diagonals." The square is:

25	18	11	9	2
14	7	5	23	16
3	21	19	12	10
17	15	8	1	24
6	4	22	20	13

The total along the usual lines is 65. The total along the broken diagonals is also this; for example, $25 + 16 + 12 + 8 + 4 = 65$, or $13 + 17 + 21 + 5 + 9 = 65$, etc.

The game we can have using this is as follows: cut out five disks from a card, as shown, and fasten them together with a little staple. Write the numbers in our magical square on the disks so that each column will occupy a radius. The numbers along a radius

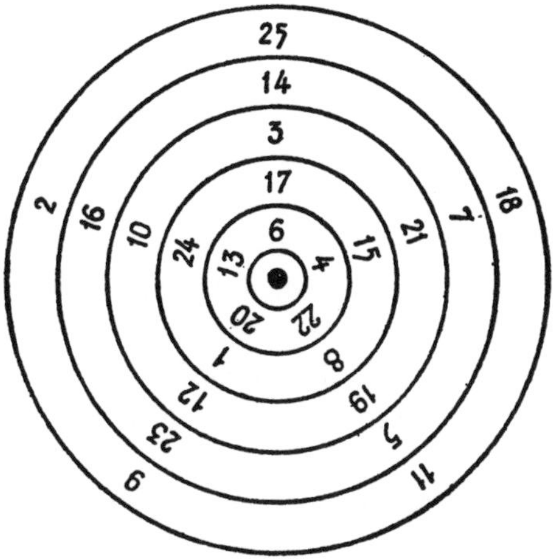

will add to 65, of course; but the total will be the same if we add the numbers spirally, e.g., 20 + 24 + 3 + 7 + 11; 9 + 5 + 21 + 17 + 13; 4 + 8 + 12 + 16 + 25; etc.

The game consists of moving the five disks at random and then asking someone to turn them so that each row of numbers adds to 65. This cannot be done easily unless perhaps by accident, and everyone will be amazed to see that the numbers added spirally also add to 65.

CHAPTER 12

SHAPES AND SIZES

The Möbius Strip

The reader might imagine that math is merely concerned with the calculation of "unknowns" from the known. But there are some branches of math which are not concerned with amounts at all. These are concerned with the intrinsic properties of an object, which do not change even though the object itself may change its size or shape. During such a change, many things are altered – the surface area, the distance between various points on the body, etc. But one property usually is constant, and this is: If we start from any point, we can trace a line to any other point on the surface area. Is there any shape or body where this cannot be done? There certainly is! A sheet or ribbon of paper is an example of this. Tracing a line from one side, we cannot reach the other side without lifting our pencil. The situation remains the same if the two ends of a paper ribbon are stuck together forming a ring. But if, before sticking the two ends together, we twist the ribbon once, the "ring" will have only one side. Let us try it!

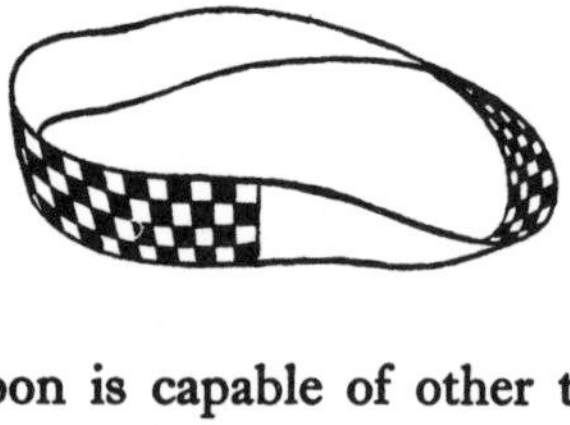

This peculiar ribbon is capable of other things, too. Cut the ribbon along its length as the drawing below shows.

We might suppose that we shall get two ribbons of the same length, but only half the width of the original one. Much to our surprise, we get only one ribbon, but it is twice as long as the original and has two twists in it.

If we cut one of these ribbons again, then we shall get two

ribbons. When we entertain our friends by showing them this, we can tell them that these are called Möbius strips.

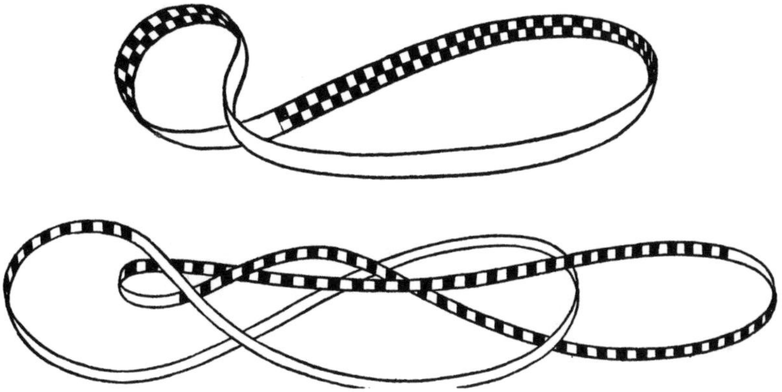

Cut the Pencil

A well-known conjurer caused quite a stir when he showed a trick in which he appeared to cut a pencil into two pieces. Without being a conjurer, we can do this trick easily; even the things needed for it are easily obtainable. All we need are an unsharpened pencil, a drinking straw, two rubber bands, and a shoelace. Fasten one end of the straw with a rubber band to one end of the pencil (*a*).

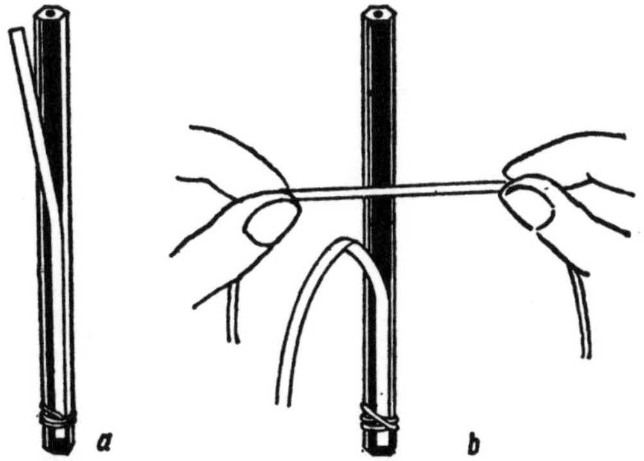

Ask someone to hold the pencil in his hand. Bend the end of the straw down and hold the shoelace across the pencil (*b*).

Knot one end of the shoelace. Cross the two ends behind the pencil so that the side with the knot on it goes over the other side (*c*).

Bring the two ends to the front and cross them over as in the drawing (*d*). Always put the end with the knot in it over the other,

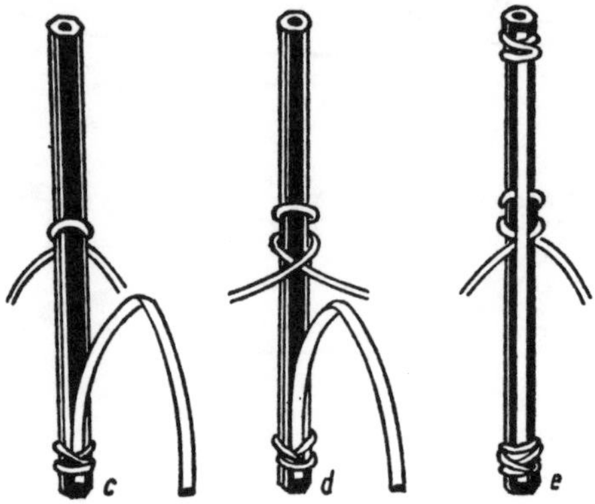

or the trick will not work. Now straighten out the straw and fasten the free end of it to the other end of the pencil (*e*). Cross the two ends of the shoelace over in front of the pencil (*f*), again behind (*g*), and once more in front (*h*).

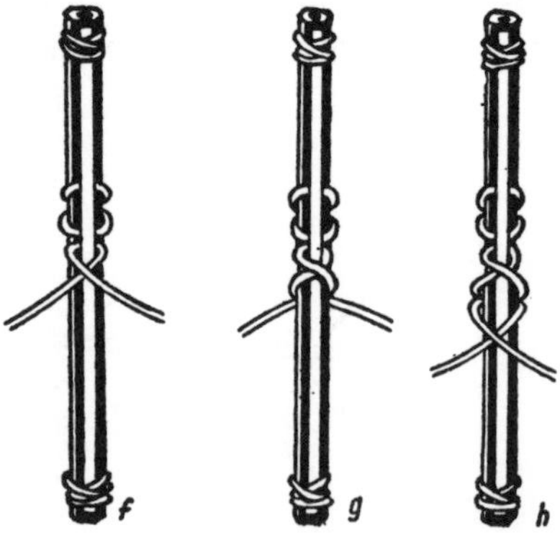

If we now give a strong pull to both ends of the shoelace, the straw will be cut in two, and it will look as if the shoelace has cut through the pencil as well, because we hold the shoelace straight in front of the pencil (*i*).

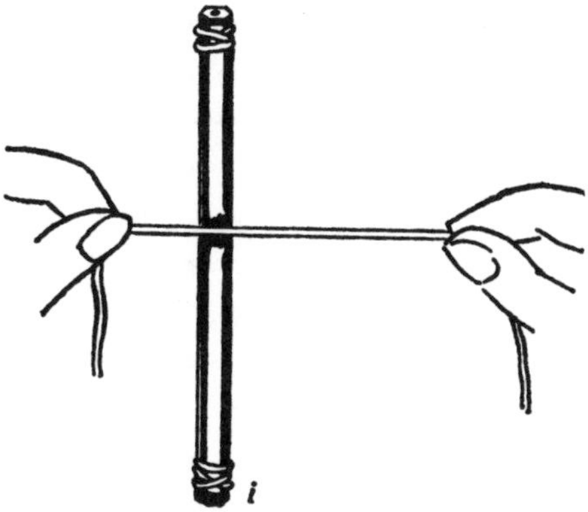

i

The explanation of this is that the turns we made before fastening both ends of the straw were canceled by the turns we made afterward. Each turn was repeated twice, really, once behind and once in front of the pencil, and so we can pull the shoelace straight.

The Game of Squares

At school we all played this game from time to time. It is played on squared paper. The players take turns in drawing a line along one side of a square and try to draw the fourth side in one or more squares. The winner is the person who has the most completed squares at the end. The game becomes interesting when it is impossible to draw a line without giving one's opponent the opportunity of completing a square.

Here one must try to give the enemy as few squares as possible.

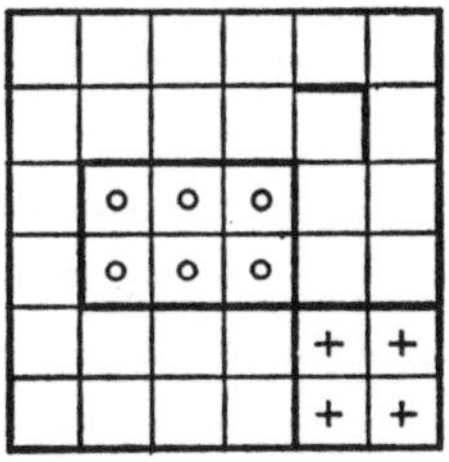

It is best to plan for this in advance and to draw lines in a small corner right at the start. The game itself calls for quite a bit of ingenuity.

A similar game can be played, using dots. The dots are drawn in lines running diagonally, as shown in the diagram.

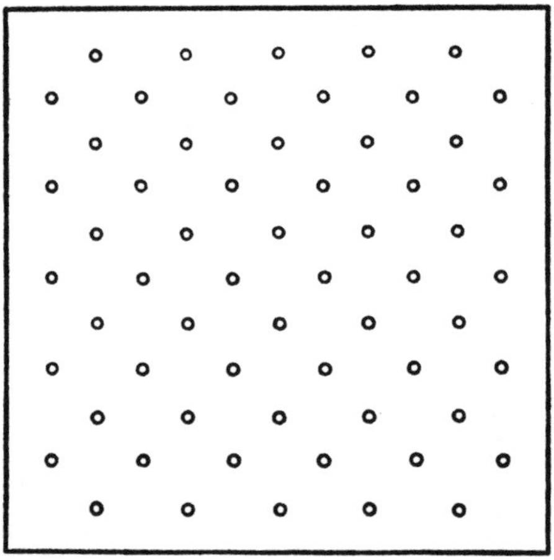

Here there are two players who draw lines alternately, vertically or horizontally. One draws with a red pencil and the other with a black pencil. The red wins when he can draw a continuous line connecting the top with the bottom of the page. Black wins if he can connect the two sides. One player cannot cross the lines drawn by another.

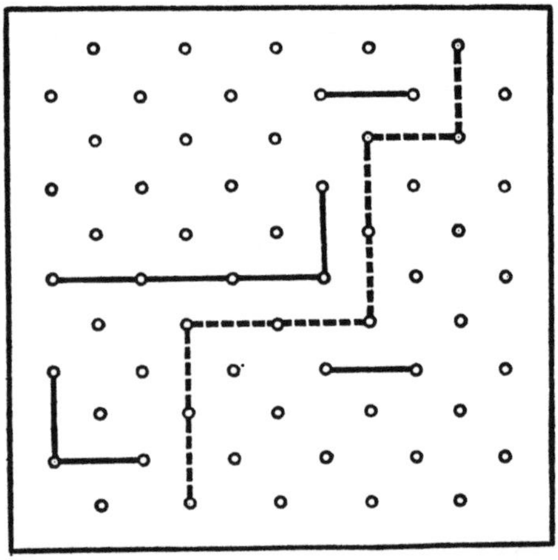

Our diagram (on which red is shown by broken lines and black by continuous lines) shows a game where red was the winner.

During the game we must watch not only our own moves, but keep an eye on our opponent, so that we can stop him winning by drawing lines across his path.

Let us suppose that Susan and Paul are playing this game. Paul is black and Susan is red. Susan is playing from top to bottom and Paul from left to right. Susan starts. She must draw her first line from the top, but where should she start? If she starts toward the left, then Paul will be able to stop her with his first move.

It is best, then, for Susan to start toward the right. Now it is Paul's turn. He must decide whether to start near the top or near the bottom. Obviously, he will be better able to stop Susan if he starts from the second dot in the left-hand column; but should he attempt to reach the side? If every player concentrates only on reaching the other side and does not try to stop the opponent, the game loses its interest, as the one who starts will always win. Paul, therefore, decides to start by trying to hinder Susan.

Such a move is not necessarily wasted, since the broken lines can be joined during the game, and a surprise victory can be achieved.

We have given only an outline here. No precise formula can be given for winning because of the many possible variations. The person who is winning can usually foresee the opponent's moves.

A String Game

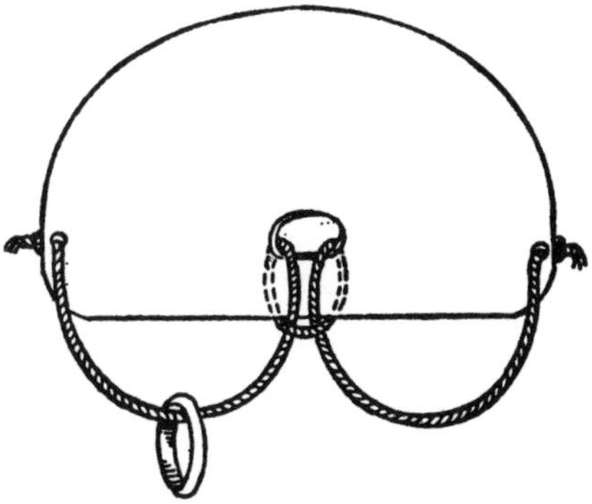

We saw during the pencil–shoelace–straw game that the position of the turns was the secret of the trick. Substantially the same principle applies to the following game. When the diagram is followed, the things needed are easily prepared. One merely needs some cardboard, some thin string, and a ring which is too large to go through the hole in the center of the card.

The string must be tied exactly as shown; the loops in the

center must be absolutely correct. Notice that the two cords from the central hole pass *under* the horizontal end of the loop. If we neglect this, the trick will not work.

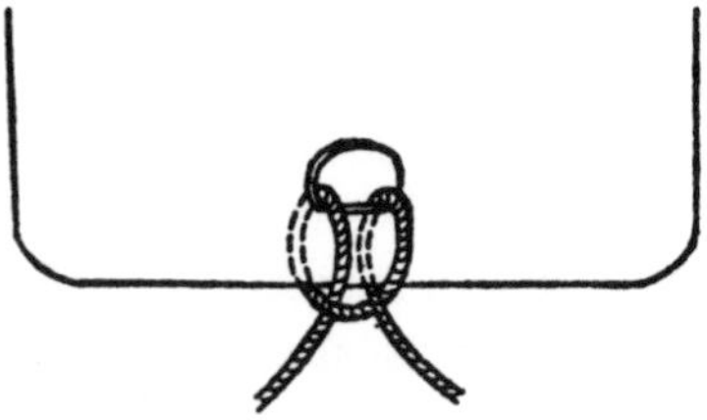

To start with, the ring should be on the left-hand loop. The problem is how to transfer the ring to the right-hand loop. One cannot slide it along the string, as the ring cannot pass through the central hole. It is easy to discover that the central loop should be loosened so that the ring will pass through. This brings us a bit nearer to the solution, and now we must really think hard! As we know, the ring will not pass through the hole in the card, but it will go through the loops at the back of the card. Since we cannot take the ring through the hole, then we must bring the loops around to the front. Therefore, we pull the two strands hanging vertically until the loops at the back come through the hole to the front. These can be put through the ring, which can then be slid over onto the right-hand loop.

Paper Folding

There is no need to airily dismiss the folding of paper as "kid stuff" just because children at nursery school do it. They can make boats, cups, hats, etc., but the examples which follow demand much closer attention than a small child would be able to give and only those who can follow the three-dimensional figures shown in the diagrams can do them.

It is interesting to realize what an important part the folding of paper plays in the lives of some of the people of the Far East – particularly the Chinese and Japanese. The folding of paper in these countries has become almost an art, which is called origami in Japan.

Pictures of eighteenth-century Japan show birds made of paper as kimono decorations. Japanese children learn paper folding at school. The practice of origami spread from the East and is particularly well known in Spain and America, where scientists and artists use it in various ways.

Traditional origami consisted of making models of animals, birds, fish, etc., by the folding of a single sheet of paper. No cutting or gluing was allowed. These restrictions are not enforced in modern origami. A little cutting here and there or a bit of gluing is quite permissible.

It is an interesting experience to convert a single piece of paper with its regular measurements into an artistic decoration.

Most simple problems in paper folding are concerned with the making of polygons, e.g., an isosceles triangle, a square, or a regular hexagon or octagon.

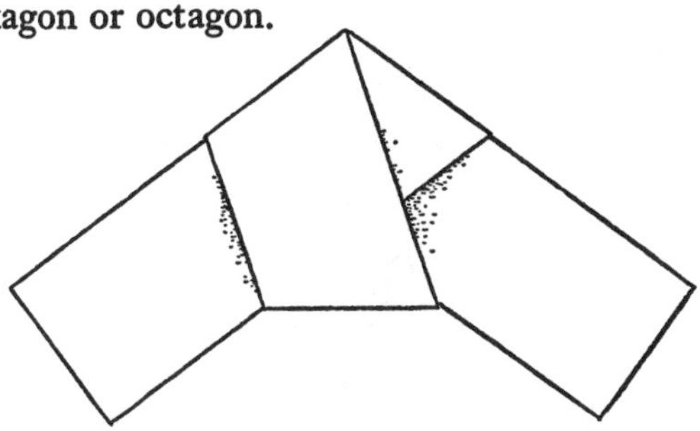

The making of a regular hexagon is quite difficult, even when a rule and a compass are used, but by folding, it is surprisingly simple.

The simplest way is to tie a knot in the paper and then to smooth it out. This solution has an extra secret. Fold the right-hand side of the strip over the knot and hold the whole thing up to the light; you will see a rather splendid five-pointed star.

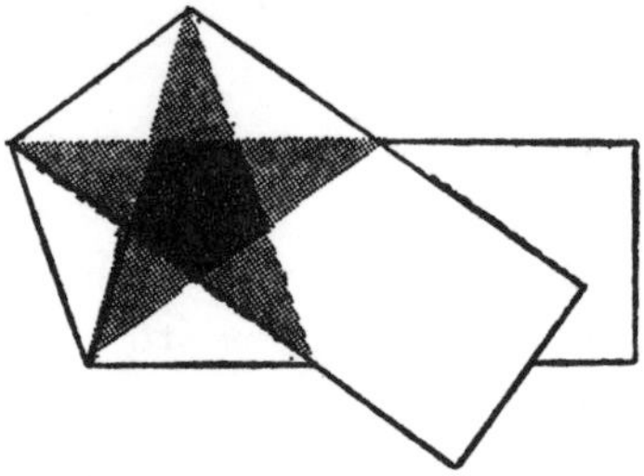

The three-sided sheet. We are used to a sheet of paper having only two sides. How can a piece of paper be folded so that it has not two but three sides?

Take a strip of paper, rule squares as shown, cut it out, and number the squares as in the diagram.

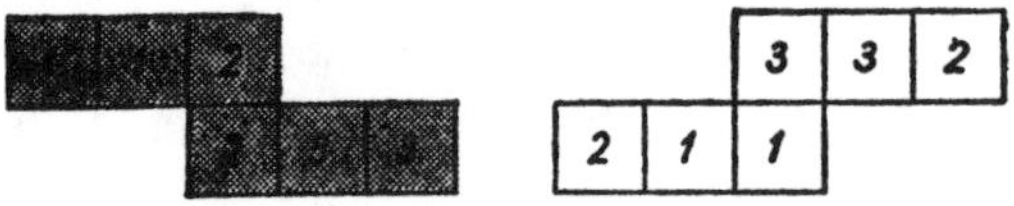

Here are two pieces of advice: Make the squares larger than in our diagram; make them about 2 inches square. The two sides of the paper should be distinguished by lightly shading one side with a pencil.

Now fold the upper number 2 on the left, behind the other number 2, and fold the number 3 nearer the edge behind the other number 3, and you will get this:

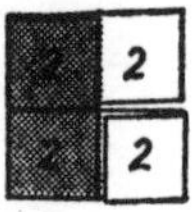

Now stick the edges together as shown, with sticky tape,

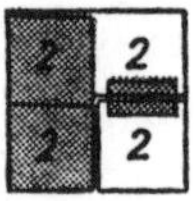

and the three-sided sheet is ready. You are now looking at side number 2, and you turn it over to see side number 3. If you fold it along the line which runs between the squares marked with a 2 and pull it open, you will see the third side, labeled 1.

The trick can be made more interesting if, instead of numbering, you color the squares.

A four-sided sheet. Here we start with a sheet which has three squares along one side and four squares along the other. Cut along the dotted lines and you get some squares which are attached to the rest by one side only.

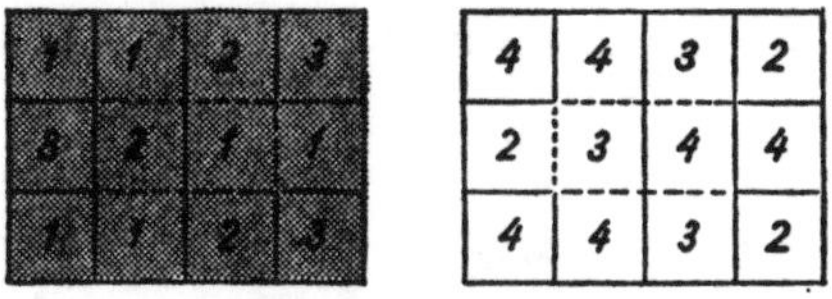

Fold these back, as well as folding back the column on the right:

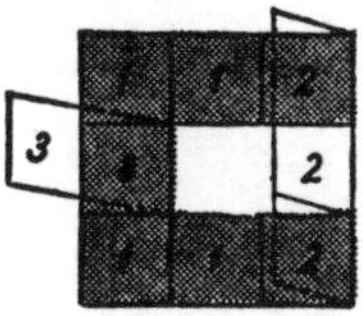

The little "tongue" of paper is folded back, the row of number 2's is folded underneath, covering the window, and we stick it together as shown, so we are left looking at squares all numbered 1 and at squares numbered 2 on the reverse.

If the side with the 2's is folded back along the center line and then opened, the number 3's are seen on one side and the 2's on the other. If the 3's are folded back and opened, then we shall see the 4's on one side and the 3's on the other, so having four sides from one sheet.

Even more sides. Similarly, we can make a six-sided sheet. Cut out and number a shape as the diagrams show.

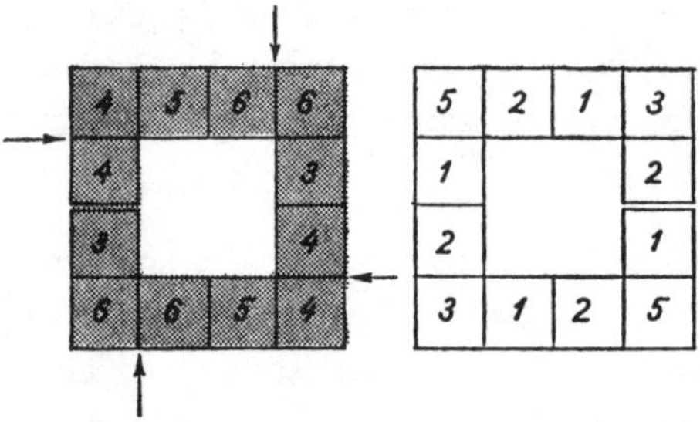

Cut through the square as shown. Following the diagram, fold forward on the line between the two 4's, as shown by the arrow on the right-hand side.

Fold forward the little tongue formed by the two squares from left to right along the line between the two squares marked 6.

Fold the lower part of the edges of squares 5 and 2 over the other part.

Fold one square marked 4 over the other on the right.

Also fold the sheet back at the lower edge of the square marked 2.

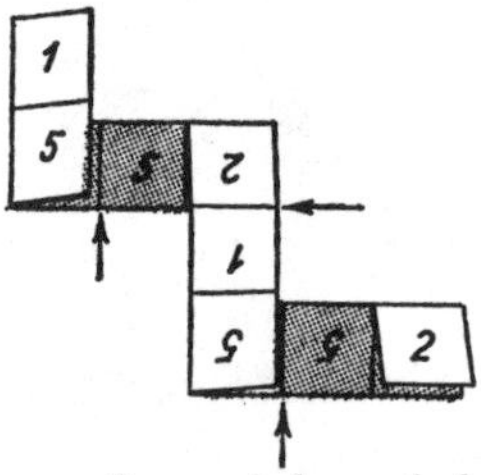

Fold back the upper row from right to left along the line between squares 2 and 1.

Put one 5 over the other, so that a square marked 2, now upside-down, is at the top. Now glue the whole thing together as shown, and our six-sided surface is ready.

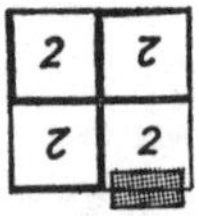

On the top the squares are marked 2; on the back they are marked 1. If we fold back along the middle and then open it, we shall see the squares marked 5; and when this is repeated, the squares marked 6 are revealed. If we want to see the 3's and 4's, then we should fold back through the other center line of the squares marked with 2.

Turn it in, turn it out. Paper folding can give even more surprising results. For example, we can turn a tube inside out merely by folding.

Mark and cut out a piece of paper with squares on it as shown.

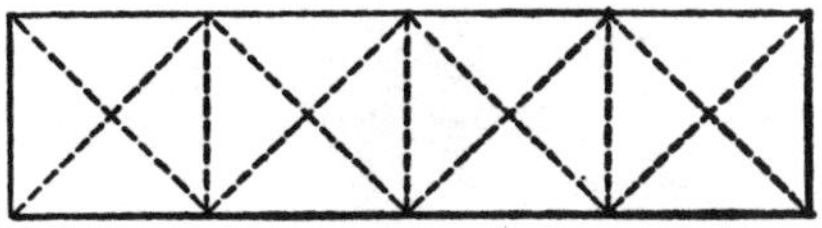

Fold lightly along the broken lines in the diagram. Now, by folding along the edges of the squares and sticking the edges together, we get a tube with a square cross section.

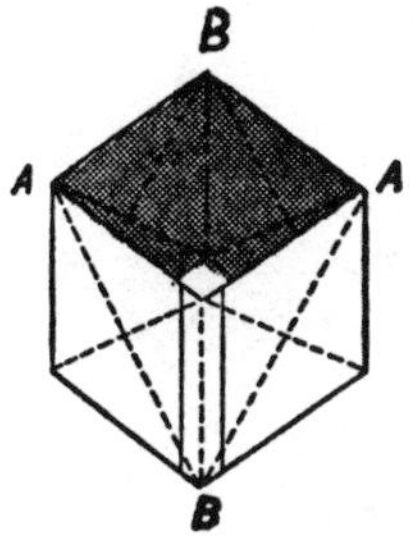

The trick consists of turning this inside out, so it is best if the two sides of the paper are colored differently. Let us turn the glued edge toward us. The upper corners, which we are holding, we will call A, and the two lower ones B. Now fold along the diagonals so that the two corners A are next to each other.

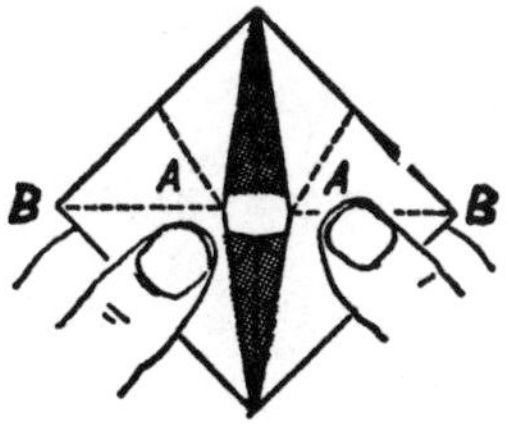

Now fold this square along the opening so that the corners marked B are on the outside.

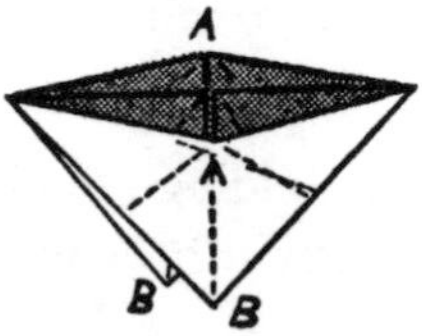

We get a triangular bag, which we should open a little, as shown in the diagram.

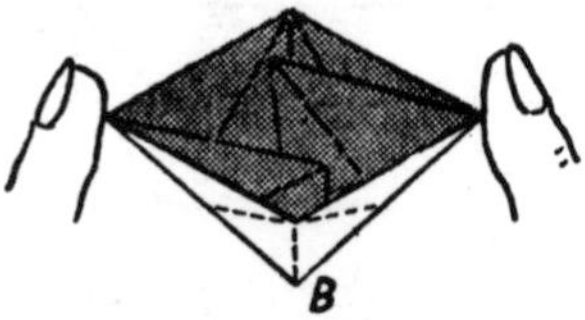

Bend the point in the right hand back, and that in the left hand forward, and we get a square, as shown in the next diagram, with point C in the center and the two corners B next to each other.

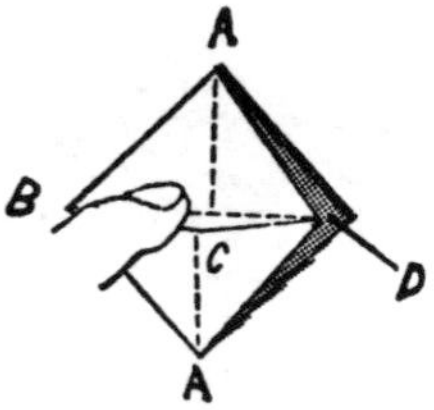

We pull slowly at point C.

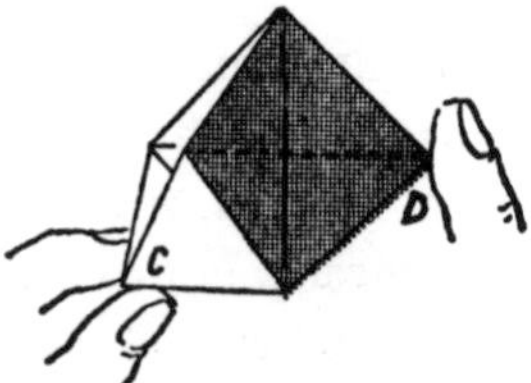

Let us mark the corner in the right hand D, as in the drawing. If we push D through to the other side, we get an envelope shape.

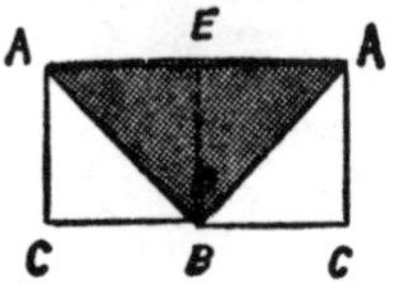

The whole can be made into a tube that will be half the width of the original.

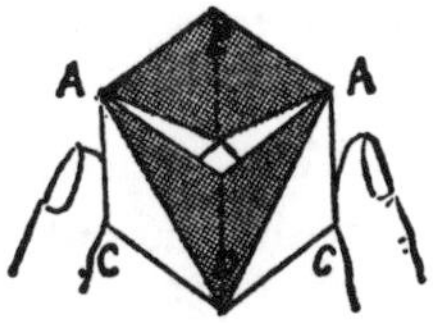

Fold the tube flat, so that the letters are arranged as shown.

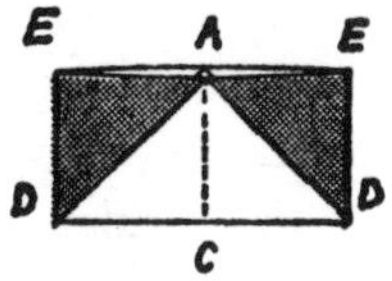

Push point E a little to the left.

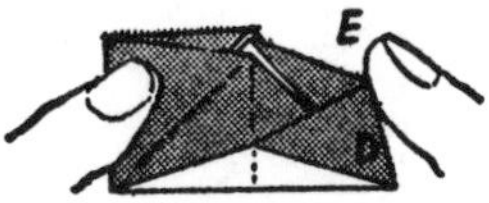

If we push the point in the left hand between the two layers and then open the square into a triangle, the turn is completed. The whole thing can be turned into a tube, and the outside is now on the inside.

The wonder bird. "Doctor, how much longer do I have to stay in bed? My temperature is nearly normal now."

"If you don't want it to go up again, I'm afraid you'll have to stay in bed until it's quite normal."

"How awful; I'm bored to tears; I'm even sick of reading!"

Just then Aunt Jane came into the room. She was usually very good at amusing children. Andy looked at her hopefully, but he was disappointed to see that she had only her handbag. Aunt Jane was quick to notice this and said, "Andy, I have thought of something to amuse you. We shall make a wonder bird out of paper!"

Andy could not imagine what she meant and watched closely as she took a sheet of paper and a pair of scissors out of her bag and asked for a pencil and a ruler. She cut out an eight-inch square.

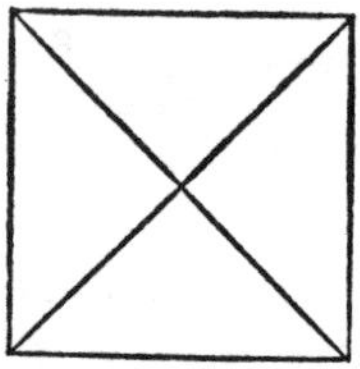

She folded it along the two diagonals; then she turned the sheet over and folded the paper through the two lines connecting the centers of the four sides.

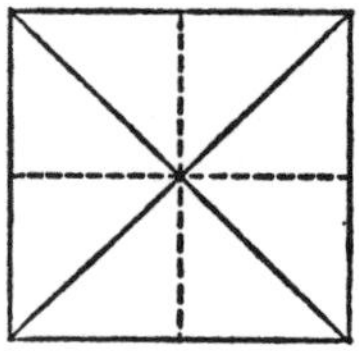

Our diagram shows the result. The broken lines show the "valleys" and the continuous lines the "hills." She folded each two adjacent sides together.

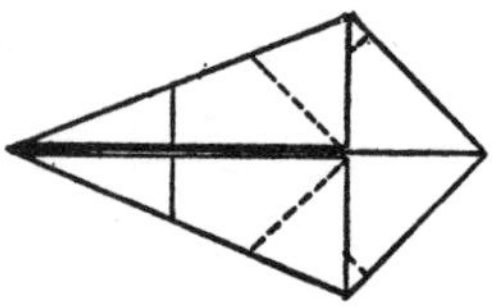

When she had folded the paper in this way at all the four corners, the sheet was opened. The paper was covered with a network of creases.

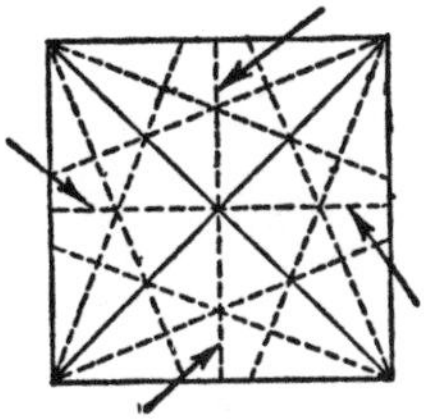

She pinched the four sections (as the arrows show), so these were raised. This pulled the centers of the four sides inward.

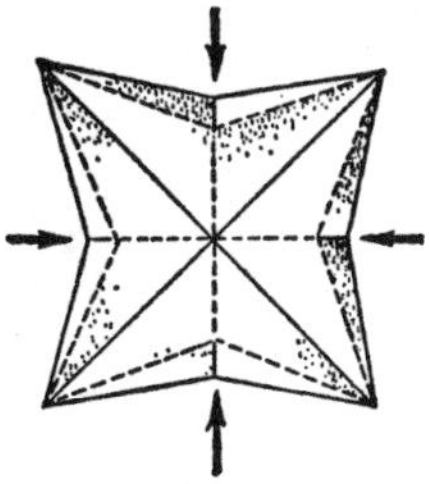

The peaks J, K, L, and M became raised as shown:

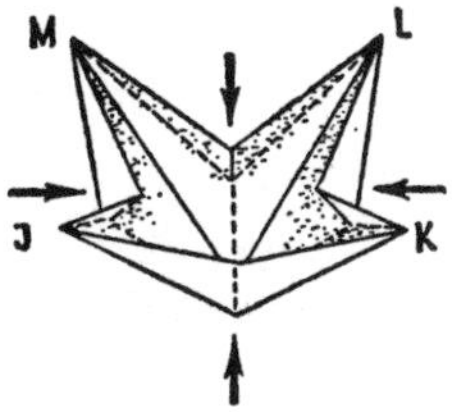

until the four points came to the top and the center of the square remained at the bottom.

The whole thing was then flattened.

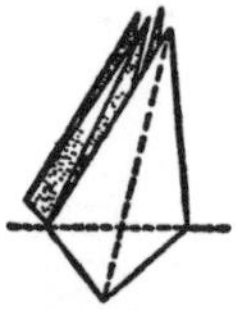

The points at the top were folded down along the broken lines; the whole was then turned upside down and the other points folded too.

The point on the right should be folded along the broken line toward the left; and similarly on the other side.

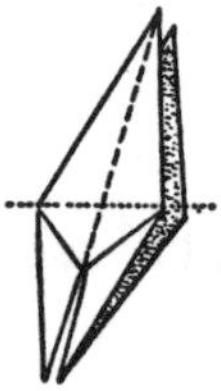

The points at the other end are folded in the same way.

She pulled the points marked A and B down, as shown in the drawing.

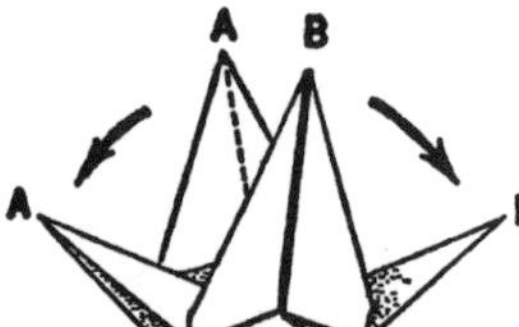

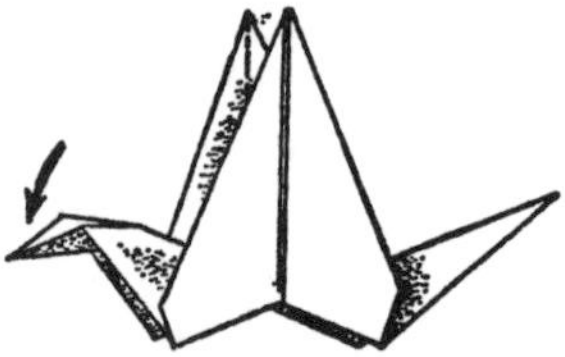

She flattened the lower half of the points that were pulled out, so the shape could be stood on a flat surface. The corner A is bent down, and the fold that ends at A is creased so that a bird's "head" is formed. The wings are easily bent out and forward, and the bird is held as shown.

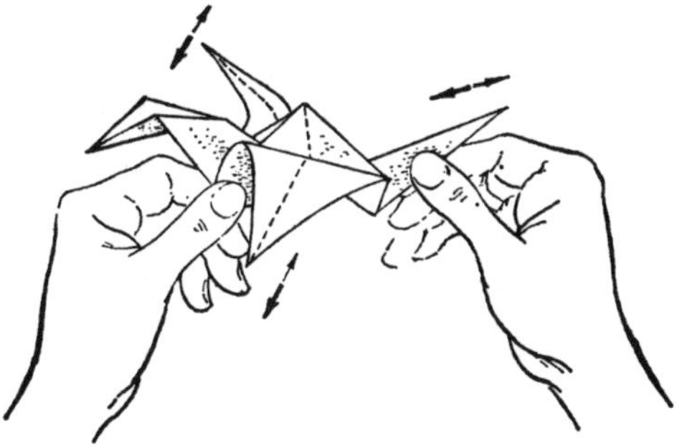

When Aunt Jane pushed the tail of the bird backward and forward, the bird gracefully flapped its wings. A wonder bird indeed!

CHAPTER 13

MAZES

At Hampton Court Palace and in many other places one can find a rather peculiar sort of construction consisting of little paths and blind alleys divided by hedges or walls.

The whole thing is designed to confuse the visitor, and he can easily lose his way in it and sometimes needs help to get out. These mysterious series of paths and turnings are known as mazes or labyrinths. Everyone has heard of them, but probably few people know that they have existed for a very long time. Excavations of ancient buildings have uncovered many decorations which resemble mazes. In the Greek myths the story of the maze of King Minos is told. The ancient Greeks reckoned this maze among the seven wonders of the world.

According to the myth, a monster son was born to Minos, the King of Crete. The monster was half man, half bull, and he was called Minotaur ("Taurus" means "bull"). The King wanted to hide the monster from his people, so he ordered Dedalus, a famous master builder, to build a special palace from which no stranger would return. Dedalus built the labyrinth, and the

Minotaur was shut into it. Dedalus was kept prisoner by Minos and escaped with his son Icarus, according to the legend, by making wings out of feathers stuck together with wax and flying away. They were said to have been the first men to fly.

It is true that the flight had a sad ending. In vain, Dedalus warned his son not to fly too high, telling him that the heat of the sun would melt the wax. Icarus loved the sensation of flying so much that he went too high, the wings dropped to pieces, and he fell into the sea.

Minos defeated the city of Athens and ordered the Athenians to send seven boys and seven girls to Crete every nine years as a sacrifice to the Minotaur.

An Athenian prince, Theseus, volunteered to go with the young people who were to be sacrificed and promised that he would kill the Minotaur. He was worried, however, that even though he might kill the monster, he would still die, because he would not be able to find his way out of the maze. King Minos' daughter Ariadne took pity on Theseus and gave him a ball of thread. She told him to tie one end of the thread to the entrance and to gradually unroll the ball as he penetrated deeper into the maze. When the Minotaur was dead Theseus had merely to follow the yarn back to the beginning and thus find the exit. Theseus escaped in this way and married the beautiful Ariadne.

Herodotus, the Greek historian, describes an Egyptian maze which had 3,000 rooms. The Romans frequently used a maze-type pattern on mosaic floors, and the Roman emperors had a pattern of this type on their clothes.

It was also a popular pattern in the Middle Ages and was frequently used for the decoration of floors and walls in churches.

In England, according to legend, Henry II built a maze in the

twelfth century. Later, in 1690, William of Orange built the Hampton Court maze. This remains to the present day, and its shape is shown on p. 157.

What is the connection between mazes and mathematics? The maze presents a mathematical problem which is similar to the problems we talked about in the beginning of Chapter 12.

If the plan of the maze is drawn on a rubber sheet, the problem of finding the correct path remains the same, no matter what shape the sheet of rubber assumes.

In general, once we can draw the plan of a maze, we can find our way about it more easily than when we are dealing with a maze of unknown plan. The best-known method of finding one's way to the middle is to enter a maze keeping one hand (always the same hand) brushing against the wall. Using this simple rule, we can find our way about, in even very complicated mazes, because we know what to do at every turning. Once the middle is reached and we continue to use the same rule, we shall eventually get back to the entrance. But if the middle is surrounded by one or more closed circuits, then this method no longer works, and we shall end up by going around and around the largest of the circuits and would never even reach the middle. The following maze (A) contains no separate circuits, and all the paths are connected. With the "hand-touching" technique we can easily walk to the middle and back.

(A)

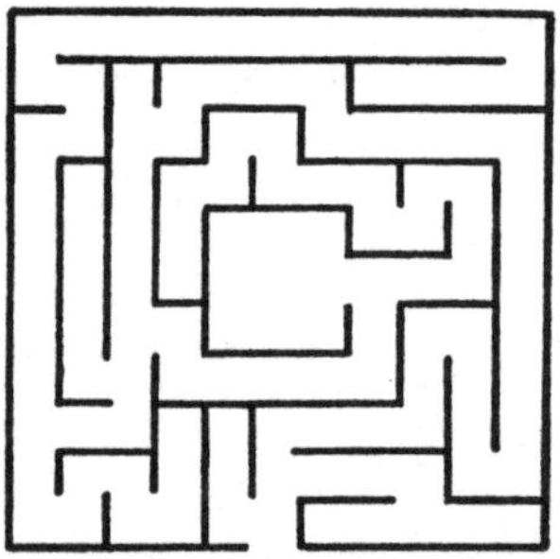

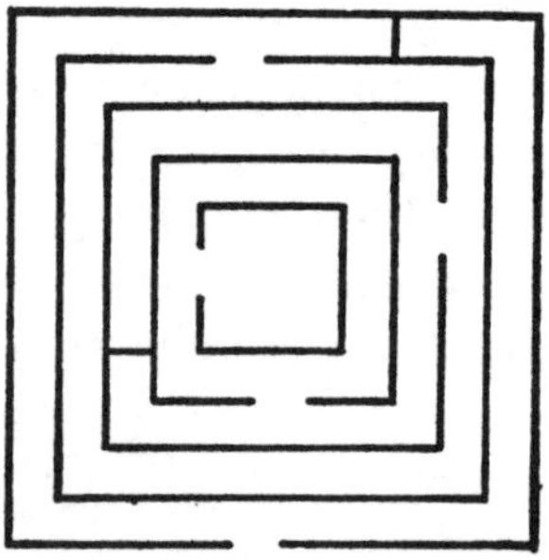

(B)

The second drawing (B) shows a more complicated example. The middle is separated from the rest, and many of the paths are not connected. Here the rule we mentioned is of no help. The Hampton Court maze contains parts which are separate from the rest. Here we can use our "hand-touching" technique, because the separate loops do not surround the middle. When we walk touching one wall all the time, we shall reach the middle, but one branch path will be missed out.

The question is, can we find a method which will work with every type of maze. There is such a method. If we look carefully at the second diagram, we shall see that this belongs to the more difficult type. If, by using a pencil, we start from the entrance and draw a line along our path, keeping to the right, we shall reach a crossroad. Here we can choose which way to go. If we find that we are back on a path we have already been on, we can turn around and go back the way we came. If we have already covered the left-hand side of a path and reach another crossroad, we can choose any path except the one we have returned on. We must never go along the same path a third time.

We shall now show you a very much more complicated maze. With a little bit of thought, and using the above theory, we can reach the middle.

It is interesting to know that the maze has received the same sort of attention as other branches of mathematics. Scientists had theories for mazes and then discovered that these theories could be used in other branches of science. For instance, they were used in automation and by men who wanted to fly around the world.

CHAPTER 14

WHERE IS THE MISTAKE?

Goethe, the German poet, once said that he preferred a young person who followed his own ideas and made mistakes to another who never put a foot wrong but always followed others. Here are some exercises which, as we work through them, involve things which are impossible in mathematics. Sometimes it is not easy to discover the mistake, because it is natural for most people to follow the reasoning of others without questioning it.

So be prepared!

The Clever Buyer

Mr Coleman, who is a well-known practical joker, went into an art gallery and bought a picture for £150. He went back on the following day, saying that he would like to change the picture. He chose another picture costing £300, and without saying another word, started walking out with it. When the dealer stopped him, asking for another £150, Mr Coleman said in reply: "I don't owe you anything, because yesterday I paid you £150, and today I returned the picture worth £150. These together are worth £300."

Where is the mistake in this reasoning?

On the first day he collected a picture and the next day he returned it. Besides this he gave only £150 to the dealer.

A Silly Argument

The population of the earth in ancient times was considerably smaller than it is today. If, however, we consider that everybody living today has two parents who each had two parents themselves, that is, four grandparents, eight great-grandparents, and sixteen great-great-grandparents, etc., we arrive at the conclusion that in the past the number of people on the earth must have been very much larger than it is now. If we take 30 years as one generation, then 300 years ago there must have been 1,000 times as many people as today. Yet it is a well-known fact that this is not so. Where is the mistake?

The mistake in this reasoning is that several people had parents in common, and even more had grandparents in common. If every couple had only one child, the population of the earth would fall rapidly.

The Counterfeit Note

A stranger walked into the local sweet shop and bought chocolates for six shillings. He paid with a ten-shilling note, which they could not change, and so the shopkeeper went next door to the tobacconist, who was able to change the note for him. The shopkeeper returned with the change, gave the four shillings' change to the stranger, who then left. The tobacconist returned the next day with the note, which turned out to be counterfeit. The owner of the sweet shop was obliged to give him his ten shillings back. How much did the sweet shop lose altogether?

Some people will say fourteen shillings, because the tobacconist got ten shillings and the stranger four. Others will add another six representing the value of the chocolate. Neither answer is right. The loss was only the ten shillings, which had to be given to the tobacconist. If this did not have to be paid, there would have been no loss.

4 = 5?

The "proof" of the next problem will be understood by older children only.

We shall prove that $4 = 5$.

Suppose	$a = b + c$
then	$5a = 5b + 5c$
and	$4b + 4c = 4a$
adding	$5a + 4b + 4c = 5b + 5c + 4a$

Subtracting 9a from both sides

$$4b + 4c - 4a = 5b + 5c - 5a$$

or

$$4(b + c - a) = 5(b + c - a)$$

dividing both sides by $(b + c - a)$ we get $4 = 5$

The mistake is in the last step, when we divided both sides by $(b + c - a)$. Since $a = b + c$, then $b + c - a = 0$, and dividing by 0 is nonsense!

A Deceptive Triangle

The class was busy studying the properties of triangles, when Peter Smith said, "Sir, I would like to prove that all triangles are isosceles."

"All right," said the teacher, drawing a triangle on the board which had sides which were obviously different. "Go ahead and prove that this is an isosceles triangle."

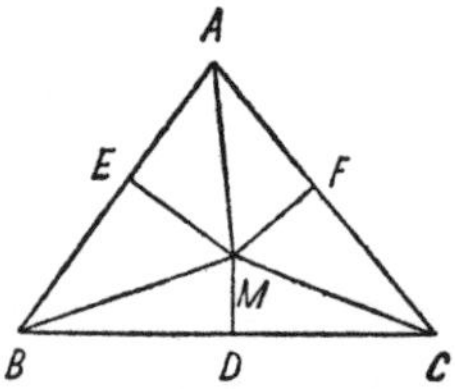

Peter took up the chalk. "Let's call the triangle ABC, and let's draw a line which bisects the angle at A, and a perpendicular at the midpoint of the opposite side, BC. These two lines will cut each other, since if they were parallel they would form one line and the triangle would be isosceles anyway. Call the point where they meet M. Drop perpendiculars from M onto the sides $\overline{AB}$ and $\overline{AC}$. Since M lies on the line which bisects the angle at A, these two perpendiculars must be equal: $\overline{ME} = \overline{MF}$.

"But M also lies on the line which bisects the side $\overline{BC}$; therefore, M is equidistant from B and C: $\overline{MB} = \overline{MC}$.

"Therefore, as the triangles MCF and MBE have two sides the same, and the angles opposite the longer sides are the same, they are congruent. Therefore, $\overline{CF} = \overline{EB}$.

"Similarly, $\triangle AFM$ and $\triangle AEM$ are congruent. Therefore, $\overline{AF} = \overline{AE}$.

"Once again, $\overline{AE}$ is the same length as $\overline{AF}$, and $\overline{EB}$ as $\overline{FC}$. If, therefore, I add $\overline{AE}$ and $\overline{EB}$, I shall get the same result as when I add $\overline{AF}$ to $\overline{FC}$. The first sum is the same as the side $\overline{AB}$, and the second the same as the side $\overline{AC}$. Therefore, the two sides are equal."

Everybody in the class started to wonder where the "mistake" was, since there must be one somewhere.

Joe Nicholson said, "You drew your figure so that the lines which divide the angle A and the sides meet inside the triangle. I think this is wrong."

Peter quickly dismissed this: "Look, if they meet outside, it's just as easy to prove that the two sides are equal. I'll draw another diagram.

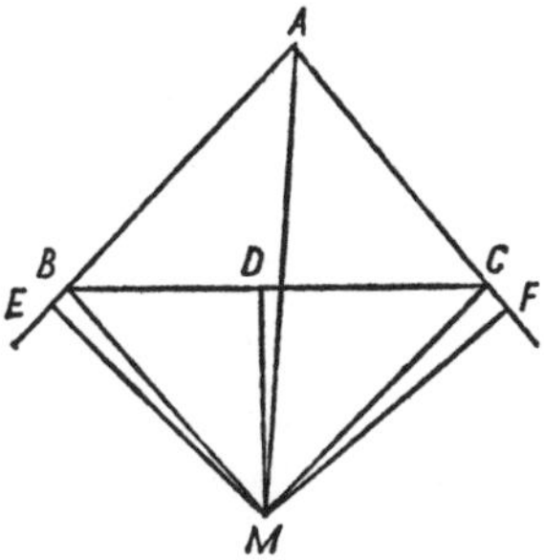

"Here the lines bisecting the angle and the sides meet outside the triangle. It's still true that $\triangle AFM$ and $\triangle AEM$ are congruent, as M lies on the line bisecting the angle at A. It's also true that $\triangle MFC$ and $\triangle MEB$ are congruent. Also $\overline{AE} = \overline{AF}$ and $\overline{EC} = \overline{FB}$. It follows, therefore, that the differences between $\overline{AE}$ and $\overline{EC}$, and $\overline{AF}$ and $\overline{FB}$, are the same. One is the side $\overline{AB}$ and the other $\overline{AC}$."

"So it is! It certainly looks like it," they all said.

The next day they prepared a more accurate drawing and discovered how Peter took them in.

It was obvious that the lines dividing the angle and bisecting the sides *always* meet outside the triangle. If we drop perpendiculars from this point to the sides which meet at A, then one will cut one side inside the triangle and the other outside the triangle.

The first side will be the sum of $\overline{AE}$ and $\overline{EB}$, the other the difference between $\overline{AF}$ and $\overline{FC}$, and the two are not equal.

When making the "diagram," one has merely to be careful that the trick remains unnoticed.

Have We Lost a Square Inch?

With a deceptive diagram we can also prove that $64 = 65$.

In order to do this, cut out two exactly similar right-angle triangles from squared paper with ten lines to the inch. Two of the sides should be 3 and 8 inches long. Cut out two trapeziums exactly the same, each having two right angles and the parallel sides being 3 and 5 inches long.

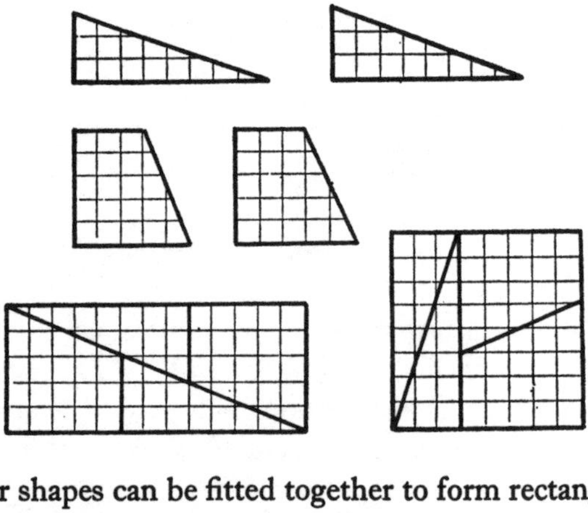

The four shapes can be fitted together to form rectangles in two different ways, as shown in the diagram.

In one case, the rectangle has sides of 5 and $8 + 5$, that is, 13 inches long. Therefore, its area is $5 \times 13 = 65$ square inches. In the other case we get a square which has sides of 8 inches, and therefore its area is 64 square inches. As both shapes were made up of the same components, their areas must be equal.

Something must be wrong!

The solution will be found only when the shapes are actually fitted together. Thinking about it, the mistake must be in the rectangle, since the square is perfect. If we put the triangle against the side of the trapezium which is 3 inches long, the answer is obvious. The hypotenuse of the triangle will not be a continuation of the nonparallel side of the trapezium, but will be at an angle to it.

A Rope Around the Earth

Let us tie an imaginary rope around the earth at the equator. To be on the safe side, we'll take a rope which is longer than we need, and the extra length turns out to be 10 meters. We tie the two ends together, and so the rope is a bit loose. Suppose that it is an equal distance from the earth at all points. Could a fly get through the gap between the earth and the rope?

One's first thought is that the gap must be far too small for a fly to get through, as 10 meters is negligible compared to 40,000,000 meters. In fact, the gap is big enough for a child to walk through, not to mention a fly!

Let us try to calculate the distance in question.

We know that we can calculate the circumference of a circle by multiplying the radius by 2π, which is approximately 6·28. The radius of the earth times 6·28 gives the length of the equator. The gap, when multiplied by 6·28, will give the extra 10 meters; or, putting it another way, the distance between the earth's surface and the rope can be expressed as $10 \div 6{\cdot}28$, that is, about 1·5 meters. The interesting thing is that if we repeat this using an orange instead of the equator, the answer will still be the same.

The question is sometimes asked: What extra distance is covered by a person's head walking around the equator, compared with his feet?

Obviously, his height times 6·28.

You might say: "All right, the calculation certainly shows this, but I can't really imagine all this."

Quite right. We must look at the result in different ways, until the answer becomes obvious.

The problem in question can be more easily understood if we think of it like this:

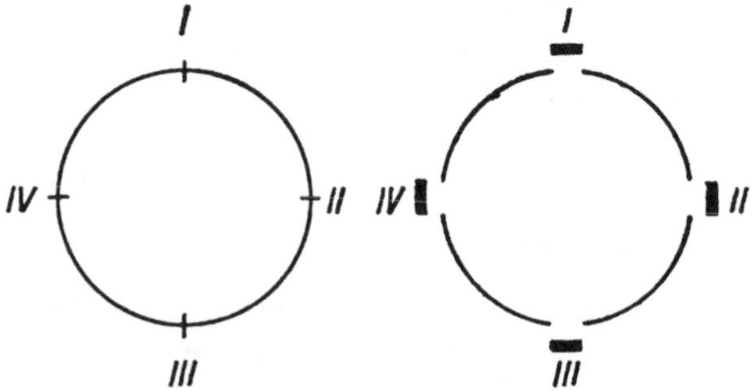

Let us draw a circle. If we want to "fit into it" an extra 10 meters, then instead of making a gap in one place, let us make four gaps and add 2·5 meters at each. Call these points I, II, III, IV.

Cut the circle at I. So that 2·5 meters can be fitted into it, one segment must be lifted up 1·25 meters and the other lowered. Similarly at II, III, and IV, the quarters must be pushed to the left and right by the same amount. We will not get an exact circle this way, but we shall get an idea of what is going on.

It becomes even easier if we replace the circle by a square. Now it will be very obvious that the extra 10 meters can be fitted in when each side is moved 1·25 meters.

We can observe this sort of thing with the collars on men's shirts. The difference in the length of two collars might be only half an inch, yet the larger collar will form a much larger circle.

A Bet

Anna and Elizabeth made a bet. Anna said that she could walk 6,000 steps in less time than Elizabeth could put 200 apples into a basket. The apples were lying in a row, each one step away from the next. Who won the bet?

Obviously – if they both moved at the same speed – we must calculate whether Elizabeth, while she was picking up the 200 apples, took more or less than 6,000 steps. To pick up the first apple, there was no need for her to move. To pick up the second, she took one step toward the apple and one back to the basket, that is, two altogether. For the third, two steps there, two steps back; that is, four. Six steps for the fourth, eight steps for the fifth,

etc. We can see that Elizabeth had to make as many steps as the sum of the even numbers: 2 + 4 + 6 + 8 + . . . 398.

We can put the question in another way. Is the sum of the first 199 even numbers greater or less than 6,000?

How can we do this without actually adding up the 199 numbers?

Let us write down the numbers twice, first the smallest to the largest, then the other way around:

$$2 + 4 + 6 + 8 + \ldots 398$$
$$398 + 396 + 394 + 392 + \ldots 2$$

The sum of the numbers one above the other is 400. We get 199 four hundreds, giving twice the number we want. The number we want is 200 × 199 = 39,800.

Elizabeth, therefore, had to walk farther than Anna, and, therefore, Anna won the bet.

Rolling Coins

Put two coins of the same size on the table. Keep one still and roll the other around the circumference of the first, until it gets back to the place it started from.

How many revolutions did the second coin make?

Without thinking, one would answer "one." If we try it, we shall see that the answer is, in fact, two, not one.

We shall understand this better if we do the following "experiment" with two congruent triangles.

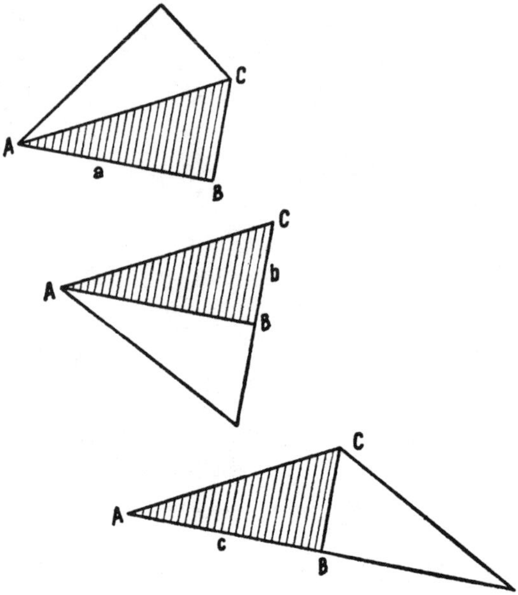

Let ABC be the triangle which does not move. Turn the other one around A till we get to the position in the second diagram. Then the triangle has made nearly one revolution. An angle which is twice the angle at A, is missing from a 360° turn. Now turn it about B in the same way, and twice the angle at B will be missing from a 360° turn, and it will be the same when the triangle is turned about C.

What will be the total of these turns? Obviously it will be three complete turns less twice the sum of the triangle's angles, that is, $2 \times 180° = 360°$. The remainder $3 \times 360° - 360°$ is exactly two complete revolutions.

Essentially, this is the same as turning one coin around another.

Deceptive Circles

We shall prove that all circles have the same circumference.

Take any two circular sheets of paper and put one on top of the other so that the centers coincide. Put a pin through the centers so that one circle cannot be moved without moving the other.

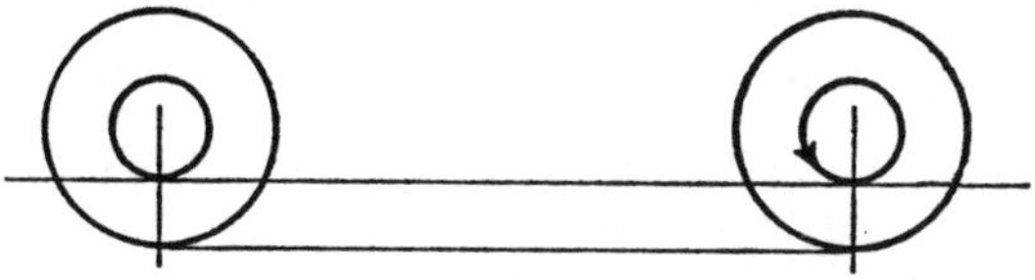

Now roll the larger disk along a straight line. Obviously when the larger disk has made one complete turn, the length of the line will be equal to its circumference. We can say the same about the smaller disk as well. The two disks moved together, so that when the larger disk completed one revolution, so had the smaller.

Therefore, the disks will give lines of equal length and, therefore, the two circumferences must be equal. Where is the mistake?

The larger disk certainly moved along a straight line a distance equal to its circumference. However, the smaller disk did not move in exactly the same way as the larger. It described one revolution of its own, but since it was fastened to the larger disk, it had to continue to move with it—but it completed the second part of its path with a sliding motion.

CHAPTER 15

MIXED PROBLEMS

In the previous chapters we were discussing problems with a common theme. In this chapter – as the heading shows – we shall look at various unconnected problems. There are some that resemble one another, but even these will give some food for thought. Most of them are designed for people who are beginners in mathematics but are quick-witted, eagle-eyed, and can think logically.

A Little Engineering

Take two exactly similar bolts. Place them next to each other as shown in the diagram.

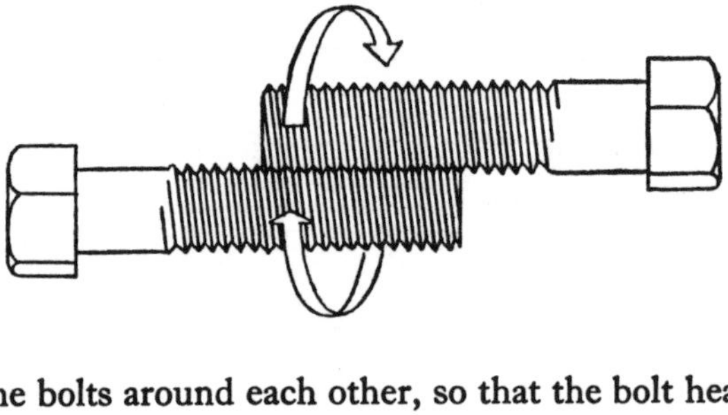

Turn the bolts around each other, so that the bolt heads do not rotate. The bolts then are moving in the same way as when we are "twiddling our thumbs."

Will the heads of the bolts get nearer or farther apart?

When we rotate the bolts around each other, they are moving in opposite directions. As one bolt head gets nearer, due to the motion of its thread, the other head moves away, for the same reason. This is similar to a person walking down an upward-moving escalator at the same speed as the escalator itself. Naturally, the person will appear to remain at the same spot.

Fly Around the World

There are a number of planes on an island. The fuel tank of each plane, when filled, contains enough fuel to take it *half*way around the world. It is possible to transfer fuel from one plane to another during flight, but there is no other source of fuel available. The pilots are told that one plane must fly around the world and that every plane must return to the island.

Now, we can see that no *one* plane can fly around by itself; it needs help from others, which can transfer fuel to it during the flight.

What is the absolute minimum number of planes needed so that one of them can fly around the world?

Suppose that three planes are needed, so that two planes can transfer their fuel at the right moment to the third. Call these A, B, and C. All three start at once from the island with full tanks. When they get $\frac{1}{8}$ of the way around the world they have used up $\frac{1}{4}$ of their fuel. C then divides its fuel into three equal parts; having $\frac{3}{4}$ of its fuel left, it transfers $\frac{1}{4}$ to A, $\frac{1}{4}$ to B, and uses the remaining $\frac{1}{4}$ to fly back to the island. (Notice that all the fuel in its tank is used up.)

A and B now have full tanks again. They fly on till they reach $\frac{1}{4}$ of the way around. Both then have $\frac{3}{4}$ of their fuel left. B then transfers $\frac{1}{4}$ of its fuel to A, because the remaining $\frac{1}{2}$ is needed so that it can return to its base. A full tank, we know, is sufficient to fly halfway. Since A has covered $\frac{1}{4}$ of the way with a full tank, it can cover $\frac{3}{4}$ of the way. Here it is met by C, who, in the meantime, has refueled and flown from the island the other way, using the fact that the earth is round. To reach the meeting point, it has used up half its fuel. It halves the remainder, so that both reach $\frac{7}{8}$ of the way, where they are met by B. To reach this point, B has used up $\frac{1}{4}$ of its fuel. It needs another quarter for the return journey, but divides the remainder between A and C. Now A, B, and C can all return to the island, A having successfully flown around the earth.

Obviously, three planes are sufficient for the job; more can do it easily. But do we want as many as three? Won't two be enough?

No, because, as we saw, the three planes used up all their fuel supply.

Six Barrels

The local wholesaler bought wines and beers in barrels of six different sizes. Five barrels contained wine and one contained beer. The drawing shows how many liters each barrel contained.

Some of the wine was sold to a hotel, and a second hotel bought twice as much. The beer was sold in the wholesaler's restaurant. The problem is, how to find out which barrel contained the beer.

Since the second hotel bought twice as much wine as the first, the total amount of wine must be divisible by 3. We know that we can divide numbers by three only if the sum of their digits is also divisible by three. The sum of the digits on the barrels give 6, 4, 1, 2, 7, 9. The sum of all these digits is 29 (which when divided by 3 gives the same remainder, as when 11 or 2 is divided by 3).

As the beer was sold on the premises, the capacity of the beer barrel when subtracted from the sum of the capacities of the other barrels should give a number which can be divided by 3. Therefore, if the capacity of the beer barrel is divided by 3, the remainder must be 2. If we look at the capacity of the barrels, we see that only the 20-liter barrel is the right size (sum of the digits is 2); $29 - 2 = 27$, which is divisible by 3. Therefore, the beer was contained in the 20-liter barrel.

The 99 liters of wine must be divided into two parts. One part is 33 liters, and the other 66 liters. The first hotel took the 15-liter and 18-liter barrels and the second the 16-, 19-, and 31-liter barrels.

An Odd Cork

How can we make a stopper from a block of cork so that it can be used to stop up a square, a circular, or a triangular hole?

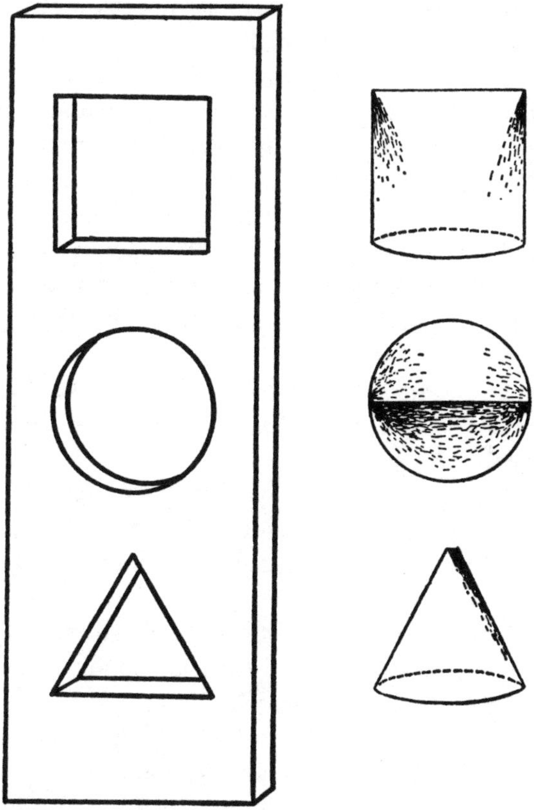

So that a bung can stop up a hole at all, it is necessary that the stopper and the hole have a cross section of the same shape and size. Other than this, the bung can be of any shape. To fit the cork into a circular hole, a cylinder is needed. This, however, is no good for the triangular hole, so we must shave two sections from the cylinder, leaving a shape as shown in the diagram.

At the same time, the cross section of one of the cylinder's ends can be square, filling the square hole.

It is interesting to notice that the cork we end up with will have half the volume of the cylinder with which we started.

A Number Game for Two or More

Anna rushed to Vera's house, where her friends Mary, Amy, and Susie were spending the afternoon.

Without saying hello, Anna said, "I've just learned a new trick with numbers! Vera, write down a three-figure number in which all the digits are different. Write the same three figures down again, so that you have a six-figure number."

Vera wrote 394, 394. Anna continued, "Don't show me the paper, but give it to Mary. Mary, you must divide the number by seven. It can be divided without leaving a remainder."

Mary was amazed because Anna was right: $394{,}394 \div 7 = 56{,}342$.

Anna said, "Without telling me the result, give the paper to Amy. Now, Amy, you divide the result by 11 – there will still be no remainder."

And she was right again: $56{,}342 \div 11 = 5{,}122$.

"Susan, you continue by dividing this result by 13 ($5{,}122 \div 13 = 394$). Write down the last result on another piece of paper, fold it, and give it to me."

Anna did not even look at the piece of paper, but passed it straight to Vera, saying, "Unfold the paper, and you will find the three-figure number you started with."

The three girls were amazed to find 394 on the piece of paper. At once they tried the sum with another number, and it came out correctly again. Then they started to try to work out why the trick always worked.

We shall tell you. When we write down a three-figure number twice, we are really multiplying it by 1,001, which can be written as $7 \times 11 \times 13$. Therefore, if the six-figure number is divided by these in turn, we shall get back to the original three-figure number.

The Merchant as Mathematician

Mary was always looking through old books, and one day she found one in which there were some interesting puzzles. One she especially liked and copied it down to show to her classmates. The solution she naturally kept to herself.

She told the story like this. An Arab nomadic tribe, for religious reasons, had to perform their evening prayers on a square prayer mat. The old prayer mat was lost one day, and they were glad that their route passed through a small town where they could buy a new one. However, the only shop in the town had one carpet left, which, unfortunately, would not do as a prayer mat, as it was in the shape of an equilateral triangle. The tribe was very upset as evening was approaching and they had no proper mat for their prayers. However, the merchant was a resourceful man, and he said that the mat could easily be transformed from a triangle into a square, with only a few cuts.

How could this be done?

Look at the drawing of the triangle ABC.

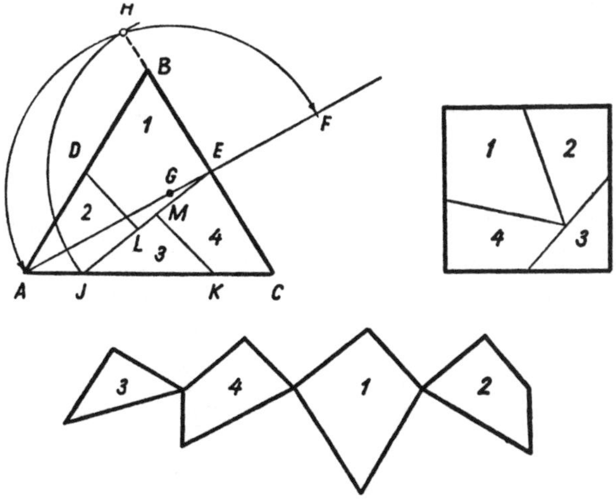

Find the midpoint of the side $\overline{AB}$ at D and the midpoint of the side $\overline{BC}$ at E. Join the points A and E and extend the line $\overline{AE}$. Measure the distance $\overline{EB}$ along this line. Therefore, the distance $\overline{EF} = \overline{EB}$. Find the midpoint of the line $\overline{AF}$, and call this G. Draw a semicircle with G as the center and $\overline{GF}$ as the radius. If we extend the side $\overline{CB}$, it will cut the circle at a point which we will call H. Then, using E as center, draw another semicircle with $\overline{EH}$ as radius. This second circle will cut the side $\overline{AC}$ at point J. Find the point on $\overline{AC}$ which is the same distance from J as the side $\overline{AB}$. Thus we shall get K. Therefore, $\overline{JK} = \overline{EB}$. Connect points J and E and drop perpendiculars from D and K onto $\overline{JE}$, getting the points L and M.

In this way we can cut the original triangle into four parts: BELD, DLJA, MKJ, and ECKM. If we fit the four together as shown, we shall get a square shape.

The Spider and the Fly

There are a number of problems in maths where the smallest or largest of a number of figures or shapes must be found.

These are not made-up problems. Many of them occur in nature and can be of help in explaining certain natural phenomena. Sometimes it is a question of life or death for a living creature to solve such problems. A spider on one wall of a room notices a fly on the opposite wall. What is the quickest way for him to get to the fly if the dimensions of the room are: length 30 ft., width 12 ft., and height 12 ft.? The spider is in the middle of one wall, 1 ft. from the top, and the fly is in the middle of the opposite wall, 1 ft. from the bottom. If the spider goes down the wall (11 ft.), along the floor (30 ft.), and up to his victim (1 ft.), he will have covered 42 ft. It is the same distance if the spider moves along the ceiling instead of the floor.

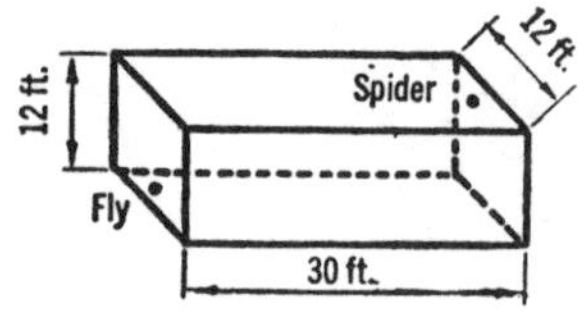

If he moves diagonally along the walls, he will cover an even greater distance, since it is well known that the hypotenuse of a right-angled triangle is longer than either of the other two sides.

How could the spider find a route shorter than 42 ft.?

The solution can be understood if we imagine the room as a cardboard box whose areas can be drawn in one plane and then the shortest distance between two points can be found. The four rectangular walls can be drawn next to one another, but the two square shapes can be fitted to the others in a number of ways. The solution depends really on this.

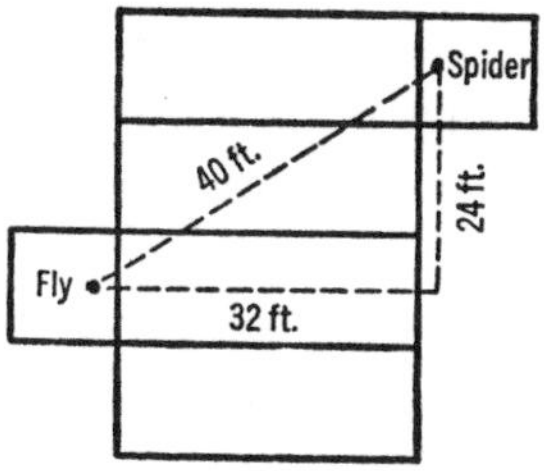

If the two squares are attached to the same rectangle, the distance between the two points will indeed be 42 ft., and so we have not gained anything. If the areas are arranged as shown above, then the distance between the spider and the fly is only 40 ft. The path between the spider and the fly is shown by the dotted line. It is an interesting fact that spiders do actually follow such a path in this type of situation.

The Fly and the Honey

This problem is similar to the one we have just discussed (with the difference that the fly is no longer the victim).

Suppose we have a glass 4 inches high, circumference 6 inches. Inside the glass, 1 inch from the top, is a drop of honey. On the outside of the glass, 1 inch from the bottom, on the opposite side, is the fly looking longingly at the honey.

At first it seems that the fly must climb vertically to reach the top of the glass. Then it must walk along the rim, then down to the drop of honey.

Let's calculate the distance involved. Up 3 inches, along the rim 3 inches, and down 1 inch, total 7 inches.

Is there a shorter route?

As in the spider-and-the-fly problem, let's cut open the cylinder. The fly will follow the shortest path to the honey.

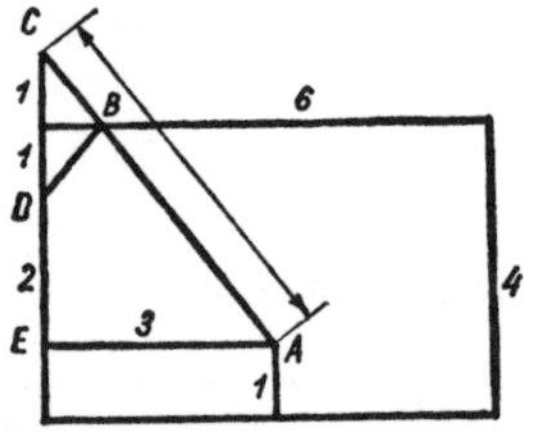

If we increase the height of the cylinder by 1 inch in theory, we shall then get a right-angle triangle in which one side, $\overline{EC}$, is 4 inches; the other, $\overline{AE}$, is 3 inches; and the third, $\overline{AC}$, is 5 inches. The fly will follow a path 5 inches long, that is, $\overline{AB} + \overline{BD}$ ($\overline{AB} + \overline{BC} = 5$ inches, $\overline{BC} + \overline{BD} = 5$; therefore, $\overline{AB} + \overline{BD}$ is also equal to 5 inches).

Will the Spider Catch the Fly?

All spiders naturally start at the middle when they are making a web. The insect goes around and around, making the web larger and larger until, when it is finished, he is at the edge. But suppose in the meantime a fly has been caught in the middle. The spider does not rush at once to the middle, but descends along one of the radii of the web, going from knot to knot. The fly can no longer escape but can also move along a radius. The two opponents move alternatively as players in a game would move.

Will the spider catch the fly, or will it escape and the spider remain hungry?

One can hardly believe that mathematics can be of help here and that the outcome depends on the shape of the web.

Suppose the web is shaped like this. And why not, since it appears to be quite "web-shaped?" Draw a web like this on a piece of card, and let one player be the spider and the other the fly. Let the spider be represented by a white button and the fly by a black one. Let us have a careful look at the drawing. The web is made up of a number of rectangles; there is only one triangle to be seen.

The fly is trying to prolong the game, and is interested in the rectangles. Since if it succeeds in reaching a position in which they

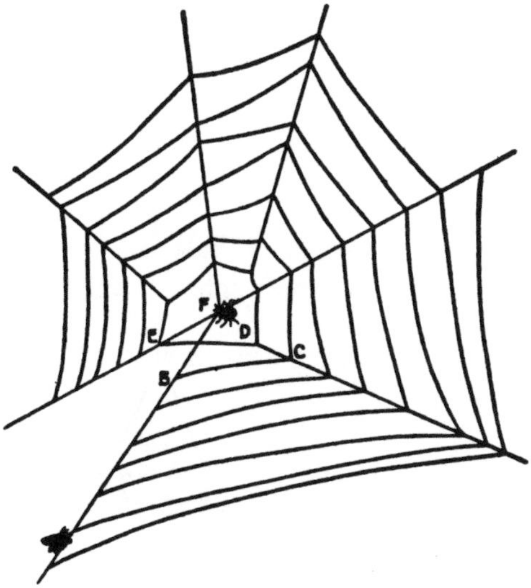

are sitting at opposite corners and it is the spider's move, the game is endless. If the spider moves to A, then the fly will move to B and the situation remains the same.

Now, the spider is not stupid either. It will try to change the order of moves. Let us observe: If it is the fly's move (it does not matter whether it has moved to A or B), it is an easy matter for the spider to catch it. The spider then would be pleased to tell the fly to move first, but the rules do not allow this. But there is the single triangle. Let us see how the same sort of thing along the sides of the triangle would change the order in which they move. The spider reaches A; the fly, observing the symmetry, cannot move away but feels safest at C, which is diagonally opposite in the rectangle.

It is no good the fly moving to B or D, so it moves to E and then to F. In the meantime, it does not matter where the fly moves; the spider will sooner or later reach a position where they will be at opposite ends of a rectangle's diagonal, and it will be the *fly's move*! Then its fate is sealed!

The Balance

Our diagram shows an ordinary balance. We are not using proper weights, but solid shapes: spheres, cubes, cylinders, and

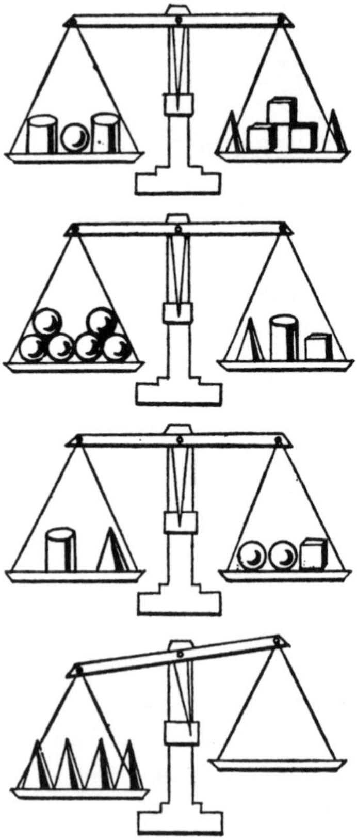

cones. The first three diagrams show the various things balancing one another, and the fourth poses the question: Which solids do we have to put in the right-hand pan so that the equilibrium will be restored; and what is the least number of solids we can use?

SOLUTION: In the third drawing a cylinder and a cone balance two spheres and a cube. The balance will not be altered if we put a cube on each pan. Then the left-hand pan will have one cylinder, a cone, and a cube on it, which is the same load as there is on the right-hand pan in the second diagram.

Comparing these two, we get: 6 spheres = 2 cubes + 2 spheres.

Therefore, 4 spheres = 2 cubes and 2 spheres = 1 cube.

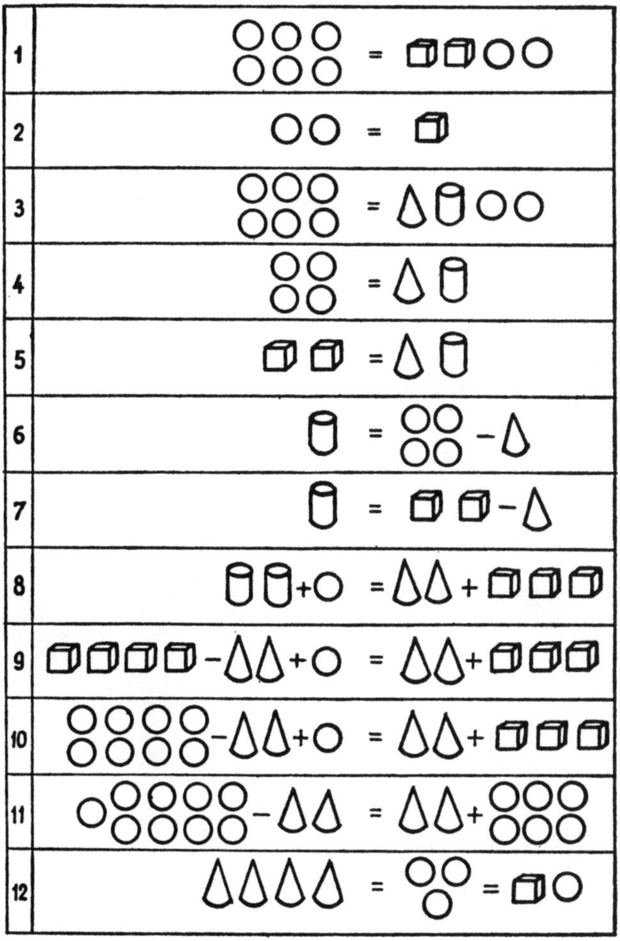

Let us put, instead of one cube, two spheres on the right-hand pan in the second diagram.

Now: 6 spheres = 1 cone + 1 cylinder + 2 spheres; or 4 spheres = 1 cone + 1 cylinder; or 2 cubes = 1 cone + 1 cylinder.

It follows therefore that 1 cylinder = 2 cubes − 1 cone and 2 cylinders = 4 cubes − 2 cones. And from the first diagram:

2 cylinders + 1 sphere = 2 cones + 3 cubes.

Using the previous equation: 4 cubes − 2 cones + 1 sphere = 2 cones + 3 cubes; 8 spheres − 2 cones + 1 sphere = 2 cones + 3 cubes; and 9 spheres − 2 cones = 2 cones + 6 spheres.

Removing 6 spheres and adding 2 cones to both pans, we get: 3 spheres = 4 cones.

So here is our answer for balancing the four cones. We can decrease the number of solid bodies needed, because we know that 2 spheres = 1 cube; therefore, 4 cones = 1 cube + 1 sphere.

A Dairy Problem

There are four black cows and three brown cows. These give the same amount of milk in 5 days as three black cows and five brown cows in 4 days. Which are the better milk producers? The black cows? Or the brown cows?

SOLUTION: Let us put a day's milk from each type into different containers. The milk from the black cows will go into small churns (we shall call these C) and the milk from the brown cows into buckets of the same size (these we shall call B). Then we can express the problem as an equation: $5(4C + 3B) = 4(3C + 5B)$; or $20C + 15B = 12C + 20B$; or $8C = 5B$.

From this it is obvious that the brown cows give more milk.

Clever Pipework

The drawing shows the waterworks, power station and gasworks. Each of them has to lay pipes to three neighboring houses.

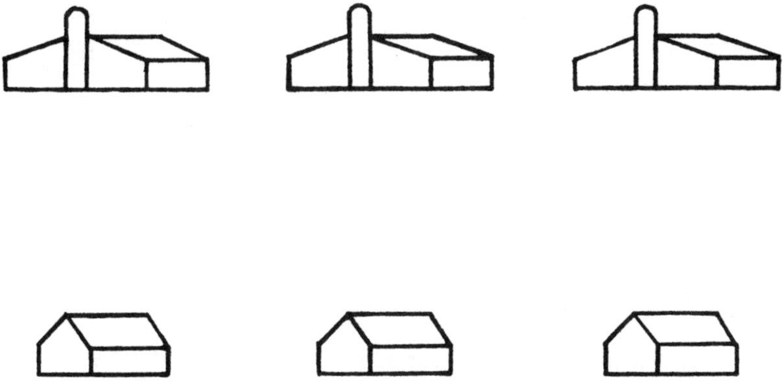

How can they do this without any of the pipes crossing?

SOLUTION:

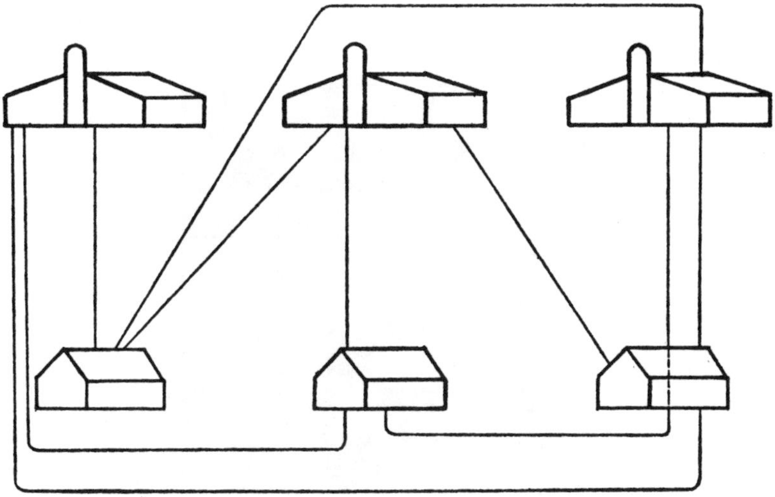

The Keen Chessplayers

George and Paul spent all their free time playing chess. The trouble was that, after the second or third game, they started quarreling. Then they would decide never to play against each other again. Usually they soon made up, however.

One day George kept losing, and he really lost his temper. In one game, when he saw he was losing again, he threw the board onto the floor, where it broke into a number of pieces, like this:

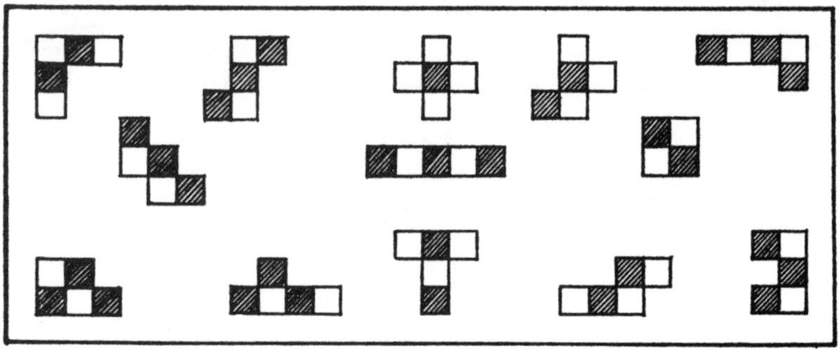

George was rather sorry for what happened, and when Paul suggested that they try to put the board together again, he gladly agreed.

They carefully collected the pieces and after a little work managed to put them together again. How did they do this?

SOLUTION:

Colored String

Penny was a clever little girl, good at solving mathematical problems. She liked solving them, but even more, she liked asking others to solve problems which she had made up.

One of her mother's friends was a math teacher, and when she was visiting one day, Penny at once tried out a new problem on her.

"Imagine that, in an ordinary room, we hammer a nail into each of the four walls, one nail into the ceiling, and one into the floor. We have pieces of string in two colors, say, blue and red. Connect every nail with every other using a new piece of string each time. The pieces of string will form triangles, one angle of which will be at the nails. The problem is, can we do this without making one triangle in which all the pieces of string forming the three sides are the same color?"

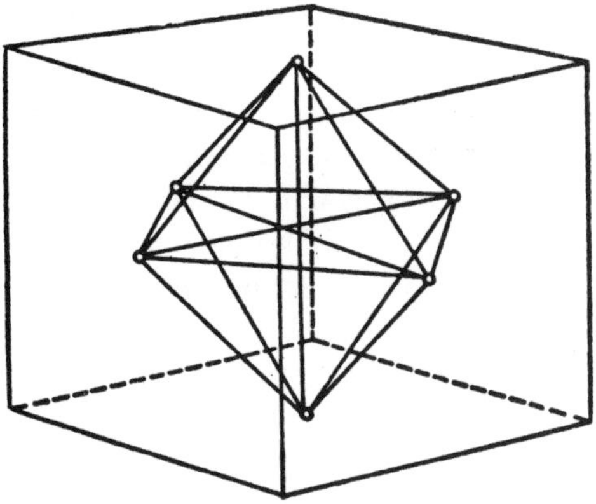

"Well, this is not an easy problem. The solution calls for a knowledge of math you don't have yet," said the guest.

"That is true," said Penny, "but I can show you the solution, all the same."

"Can you really?"

"Oh, yes. It is quite simple. The answer is that there must be at least *one* triangle in which the string forming the three sides is the same color. Let's choose one of the nails; it doesn't matter which.

To this nail five pieces of string are attached, so that one will go to each of the other nails. Since we have string in two colors only, three of the five must have the same color. Suppose that the nail is at A, and we have three red and two blue pieces of string attached to it.

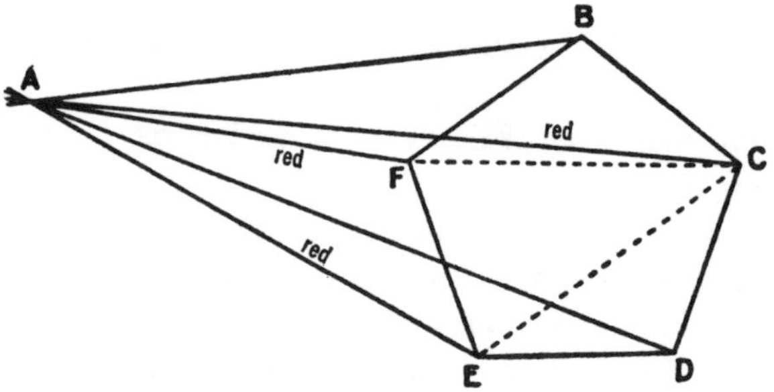

"The red strings are those which connect A with C, E, and F. If all the sides of the triangle CEF are blue, then we have found at least one triangle where the strings forming the three sides are the same color. If one of the connecting strings is red, then this is still true. For example, if CE is red, then the triangle ACE is all red. If CF is red, then the triangle ACF is all red. If EF is red, then the sides of the triangle AEF will be all red."

Penny proved that by logical thinking the problem can be solved. Many other problems can be solved by careful thinking, without advanced mathematical knowledge.

The Colored Regular Tetrahedron

One spring day the math teacher was talking about regular tetrahedrons. As he was talking, he noticed that the class was not watching the board but was looking out of the window: they would have been happier in the warm sunshine than attending a math lesson. On such occasions he would try to introduce something new and especially interesting to recapture the interest of the class; and this is what he did now. He told them of the following problem, and in no time at all the class was all attention.

We all know what a regular tetrahedron looks like, a four-sided figure, each side of which is an equilateral triangle like this:

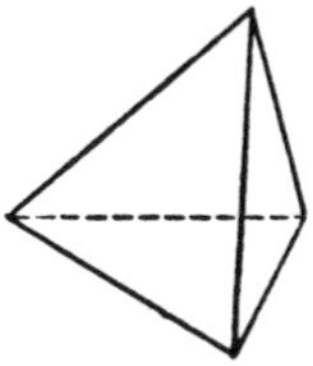

If we "open this up" to be in one plane only:

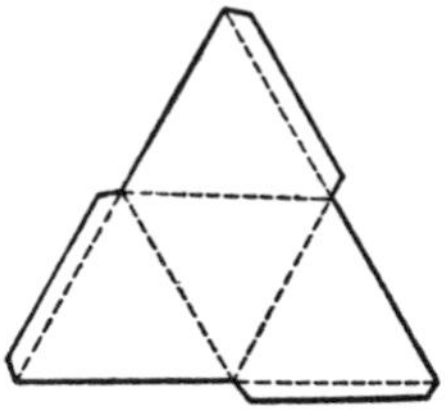

We also know that sunlight can be broken down into seven colors: red, orange, yellow, green, light blue, dark blue, and violet.

In how many different ways can a regular tetrahedron be colored so that one, two, three, or four of the seven colors are used? There are also some conditions laid down on how to do this:

1. A face can be colored with only one color at a time.
2. There should be no face left unpainted.
3. If a face which is already painted is rotated (for example, if the base painted yellow becomes a side), we cannot count this again. Also, this applies if all the four faces are red, for instance, or if two sides of the same regular tetrahedron are red, one blue, and the fourth yellow, etc.

We must confess that none of the children gave the correct answer. There were four children in the class who were fond of doing problems like this, and they met after school to talk this one over. At the next lesson they announced that they had found the "right solution." This is how Peter, the leader, explained it all:

"Let's have another look at the 'opened-up' regular tetrahedron, which makes things easier. Let us take four colors out of the seven, for example, red, blue, green, and yellow. Using these, we can find two different ways of coloring the figure.

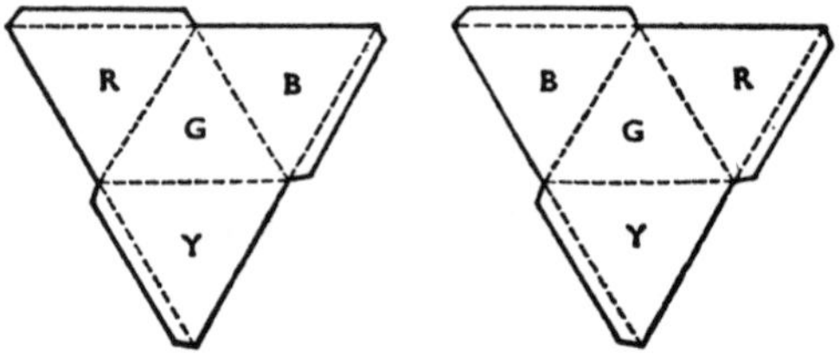

"If, however, only *three* colors out of the seven are chosen (red, green, and yellow), then there are *three* possible solutions:

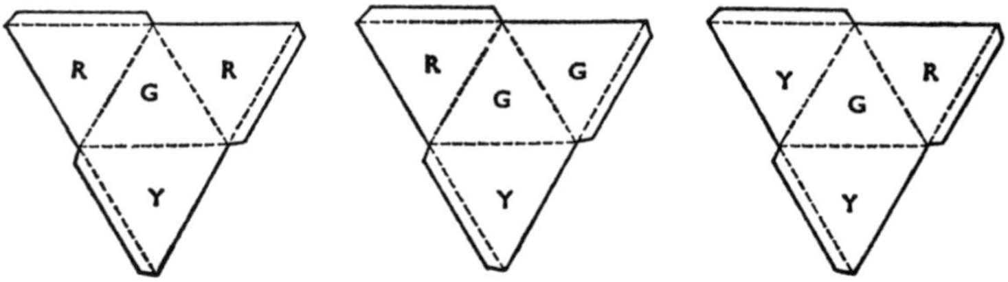

"Choosing two colors (green and yellow), again there are three possible solutions:

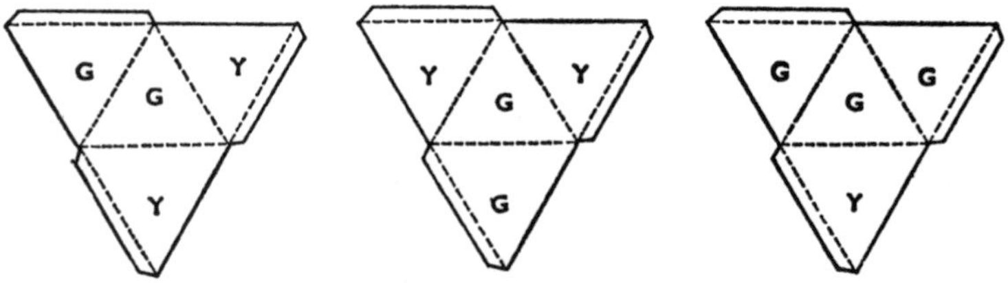

"If only one color is chosen, then there is, of course, only one way of painting."

But how many ways can four colors be chosen out of seven? In mathematics we meet this sort of problem very often. The way to solve a problem of this sort is not by trial and error, but by logical thinking, to arrive at a general rule. Let us number the colors from 1 to 7.

There will be 4	groups	beginning	with	1 2 3
3	"	"	"	1 2 4
2	"	"	"	1 2 5
1	"	"	"	1 2 6
3	"	"	"	1 3 4
2	"	"	"	1 3 5
1	"	"	"	1 3 6
2	"	"	"	1 4 5
1	"	"	"	1 4 6
1	"	"	"	1 5 6
3	"	"	"	2 3 4
2	"	"	"	2 3 5
1	"	"	"	2 3 6
2	"	"	"	2 4 5
1	"	"	"	2 4 6
1	"	"	"	2 5 6
2	"	"	"	3 4 5
1	"	"	"	3 4 6
1	"	"	"	3 5 6
1	"	"	"	4 5 6

The number of groups, then, is 35.

Using four colors, we have $35 \times 2 = 70$ different possibilities. With three colors there are 35 different possibilities, because when we choose four colors out of the seven, there are three colors left, giving 105 different possibilities. Two colors can be chosen in 21 different ways, giving $21 \times 3 = 63$; and, finally, one color can be chosen 7 different ways. The total number of possibilities is therefore $70 + 105 + 63 + 7 = 245$.

Jack and Jill

In 1945 a father was asked how old his children were. He gave the following mysterious answer: "Both children are older than 10 and younger than 20 years. If we multiply Jack's age twice with itself (that is, cube it) and we add to this number Jill's age multiplied with itself (that is squared), then we shall get the year in which my wife was born. I am five years older than my wife. How old are the members of my family?"

SOLUTION: Do not forget, all this happened in 1945. The mother must have been born at the end of the nineteenth or the beginning of the twentieth century. Therefore, only one answer is possible. If Jack were 12, then $12 \times 12 \times 12 = 1728$. If Jack were 11, then $11 \times 11 \times 11 = 1331$, which number is obviously too small. If, however, he were 13, then $13 \times 13 \times 13 = 2197$, which is too large.

Jill must have been 13, because $13 \times 13 = 169$ and $1728 + 169 = 1897$. If Jill were to be 11 or 14, we would have an impossible number. As the mother was born in 1897, she was 48 in 1945 and the father was 53 years old.

Another Problem About Age

Mr Parabola liked giving funny answers to some of the questions asked of him. He was just like a typical character in a book about math, because when someone asked him how old he was, he would give a complicated answer just to make things difficult. Once an unsuspecting acquaintance asked him how old his three daughters were. Naturally he disguised his answer as a puzzle.

"Jean's age is the same as the ages of Katie and Elizabeth added together. Kate was twice as old last year as Elizabeth was. Two years from now Jean will be twice as old as Elizabeth. Now, you can find out how old they are, can't you?"

The person who asked the question was not too good at math, so we had better help!

SOLUTION: If Jean is x, Kate y, and Elizabeth z years of age, then a year ago Jean was $x - 1$, Kate was $y - 1$, and Elizabeth was $z - 1$ years old. Two years from now Jean will be $x + 2$, Kate will be $y + 2$, and Elizabeth will be $z + 2$ years old.

Since Jean's age now is the same as that of Kate and Elizabeth added together: $x = y + z$.

A year ago, however, Kate was twice as old as Elizabeth: $y - 1 = 2(z - 1)$.

Two years from now, Jean will be twice as old as Elizabeth; therefore: $x + 2 = 2(z + 2)$.

From the second equation we have $y = 2(z - 1) + 1$; and from the third $x = 2(z + 2) - 2$.

Substituting these values into the first equation we get $2(z + 2) - 2 = 2(z - 1) + 1 + z$; or $2z + 4 - 2 = 2z - 2 + 1 + z$; or $z = 3$.

Therefore Elizabeth is 3, Kate is 5, and Jean is 8.

Good Luck!

Men have always looked for quick ways of getting rich. In the Middle Ages they used to carry around various "magical" objects or lucky charms; they thought that these would bring them good luck. Some of these were known as amulets, and we shall now show you one of these.

The Latin word *fortuna* means luck or fortune. This word was used in an amulet, like this.

They started in the top left-hand corner of the diagram with the large F, and had to reach the bottom right-hand corner, going through every square once apart from the middle one. What is more, the letters along the line should read FORTUNA FORTUNA, etc.

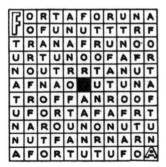

SOLUTION:

F	O	R	T	A	F	O	R	U	N	A
	O	F	U	N	U	T	T	T	R	F
T	R	A	N	A	F	R	U	N	O	O
U	R	T	U	N	O	O	F	A	F	R
N	O	U	T	R	R	T	A	N	U	T
A	F	N	A	O	■	U	T	U	N	A
T	R	O	F	F	A	N	R	O	O	F
U	F	O	R	T	A	F	A	F	R	T
N	A	R	O	U	N	O	N	U	T	U
N	U	T	F	A	N	R	N	A	R	N
A	F	O	R	T	U	T	U	F	O	A

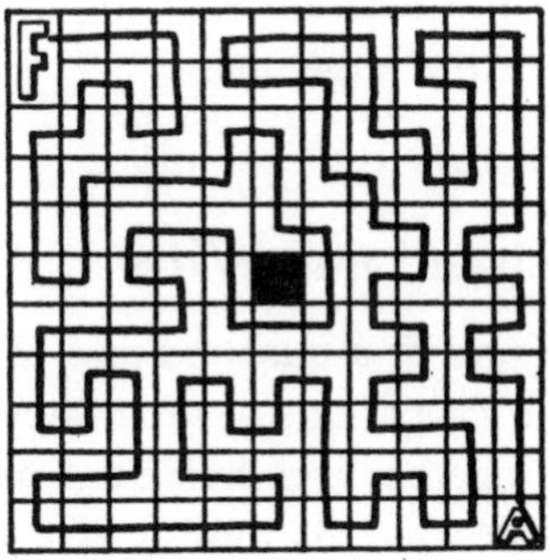

Squares from a Square

The square in the diagram is to be changed into five smaller squares, the areas of which will total that of the larger square.

SOLUTION: By connecting the midpoint of each side with the corner opposite, we get five small squares, as shown. You will see

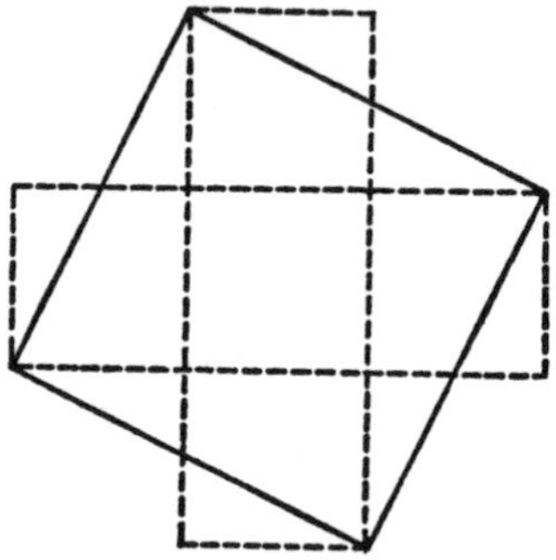

from the diagram that the areas of the small squares add up to that of the large one.

Husband and Wife

The ages of a husband and wife include the same two digits, but in the case of one of them they are turned around. If we add their ages together and divide the sum by 11, we shall get the difference in their ages. Supposing that the husband is older than his wife, what are their ages?

SOLUTION: If the husband is $10x + y$ years old, then the wife will be $10y + x$.

Adding their ages:

$$10x + y + 10y + x = 11(10x + y - 10y - x).$$

Simplifying:

$$\begin{aligned} 11x + 11y &= 11(9x - 9y) \\ x + y &= 9(x - y) \\ 10y &= 8x \\ 5y &= 4x \\ y &= 4 \\ x &= 5 \end{aligned}$$

The husband is 54 and his wife is 45 years of age.

In the next group of problems we shall show you some problems that resemble one another. They require no special calculating ability, only some common sense and orderly thinking.

You should notice that the methods used here are the same as those used to solve problems in science. First we are faced with a number of more or less related facts. The connection between some of them is obvious, but in some cases we have to make suppositions (hypotheses) before we can proceed.

Whether the hypotheses are correct or not, only the final result will show. If some of the assumptions give impossible results, then these must be discarded and new ones tried.

Who Is Guilty?

During the lunch hour, one of the windows of the classroom was broken. There were four boys in the room at the time, Andrew, Leslie, George, and Tom. The teacher asked each who broke the window? He got the following answers:

Andrew: It was Leslie
Leslie: Tom did it
George: It wasn't me
Tom: Leslie is lying if he says it was me.

Who broke the window if *only one* boy was telling the truth? Or the other way around: Who was guilty, assuming one boy was lying and the other three were telling the truth?

In the first case, only Tom was telling the truth. If we suppose that Leslie was telling the truth, then George must also be truthful; if Andrew was telling the truth, then George and Tom could not have been lying. And if what George said was true, then what

Andrew and Leslie said must have been true as well. It follows therefore that George broke the window.

In the second case, Leslie was the guilty one, because the others must have been telling the truth.

The Three Friends

Mr Barker, Mr Jones, and Mr Simon worked at the same firm and were good friends. One was the cashier, the second the buyer, and the third the firm's accountant (not necessarily in order of their names).

The accountant was an only child and had the lowest salary. Mr Simon, who married Mr Barker's sister, earned more than the buyer.

What was the job of each?

SOLUTION: The problem is not difficult; you could do it in your head. However, we would like to show a general solution which can be used in later, more complicated problems.

Draw a table like this:

	Barker	*Jones*	*Simon*
cashier			
buyer			
accountant			

The impossible we will show as o, and the possible as +.

From what we are told we can say that:

1. Barker cannot be the accountant because he has a sister. Put an o under Barker opposite accountant.

2. Simon cannot be the accountant because he has not the lowest salary.

Our table now looks like this:

	Barker	*Jones*	*Simon*
cashier			
buyer			
accountant	o	+	o

From this it follows that the accountant must be Jones.

3. Simon earns more than the buyer; therefore, he cannot be the buyer, but he must be the cashier and Barker must be the buyer.

The completed table looks like this:

	Barker	*Jones*	*Simon*
cashier	o	o	+
buyer	+	o	o
accountant	o	+	o

The Smith Family

The Smith family consists of John Smith, his wife, their son, John Smith's sister, and Mrs Smith's father. They all live in the same house; they all work, doing various jobs. Among them there are a shop assistant, a judge, a carpenter, a teacher, and a civil servant.

The judge and the teacher are not blood relations. The shop assistant is older than his or her sister-in-law and is also older than the teacher. The carpenter, who also trains a football team, is older than the civil servant.

What is the occupation of each?

The son is the only one who is related to all the rest of the family; therefore, he cannot be a teacher or a judge. Also, he cannot be the carpenter or the shop assistant because, we suppose, he is the youngest in the family.

Our table now looks like this:

	Mr Smith	*Mrs Smith*	*Smith Jr*	*Sister*	*Grand-father*
shop assistant			o		
judge			o		
civil servant	o	o	+	o	o
carpenter			o		
teacher			o		

Obviously Smith Jr must be the civil servant, and no one else in the family can be.

The carpenter is obviously a man, and therefore Mrs Smith and Mr Smith's sister cannot be carpenters. Mrs Smith and Mr Smith's sister are sisters-in-law. It follows that the shop assistant must be a woman; therefore, neither Mr Smith nor his father-in-law can be a shop assistant.

Our table now looks like this:

	Mr Smith	*Mrs Smith*	*Smith Jr*	*Sister*	*Grand-father*
shop assistant	o		o		o
judge			o		
civil servant	o	o	+	o	o
carpenter		o	o	o	
teacher		o	o	o	

The shop assistant must be either Mrs Smith or her sister-in-law, and the teacher must be either Mr Smith or his father-in-law.

Mrs Smith cannot be the shop assistant, because she would then be older than her own father. Thus, Mr Smith's sister must be the shop assistant and Mrs Smith the judge. Mr Smith must be the teacher, because the judge and the teacher are not blood relations.

So:

	Mr Smith	*Mrs Smith*	*Smith Jr*	*Sister*	*Grand-father*
shop assistant				+	
judge		+			
civil servant			+		
carpenter					+
teacher	+				

The Round Table

Seven friends – Anna, Bobby, Celia, David, Elizabeth, Fiona, and George – used to meet each day, usually at Anna's house, where, sitting around a circular table, they used to amuse each other with mathematical games. One day Anna suggested that on three successive days they should try to sit next to completely different neighbors.

On the first day they sat in alphabetical order, Anna having Bobby on her right and George on her left. Anna's best friend was Bobby, and she was not particularly fond of George. On the next two days she arranged that Bobby should sit as near as possible to her and George as far away as possible.

How did she arrange the others?

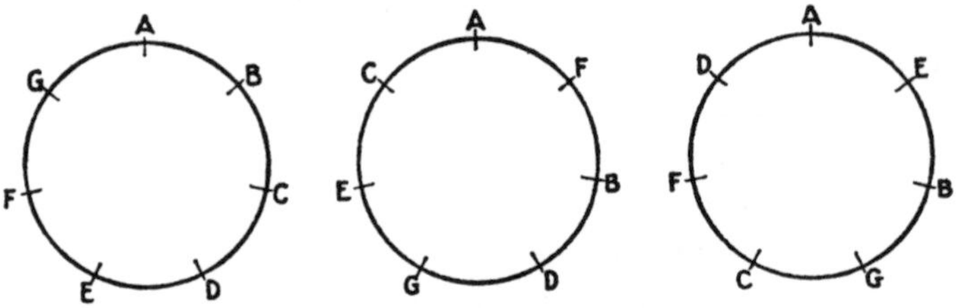

1st day 2nd day 3rd day

This proved to be the only arrangement which would satisfy Anna's wishes.

Six Ladies

Six ladies were having dinner together, sitting at a round table. Their occupations were: manager of a shop, social worker, secretary, lecturer, nurse, and the hostess, who was a housewife married to an engineer. Their names were (not in order) Elizabeth Anderson, Mary Baker, Sarah Clark, Valerie Dunn, Susan Evans, and Mrs Joe Fox. We are asked to determine who sat where at the table.

We are told that:

> Valerie Dunn sat opposite the secretary.
> Elizabeth Anderson, who was not a social worker, sat opposite the manageress.
> The lecturer sat on the left of the social worker.
> The wife of the engineer sat opposite Mary Baker.
> Mrs Joe Fox sat on the right of Elizabeth Anderson.
> Valerie Dunn is not a manageress.
> The nurse sat opposite Susan Evans.

Where did they all sit?

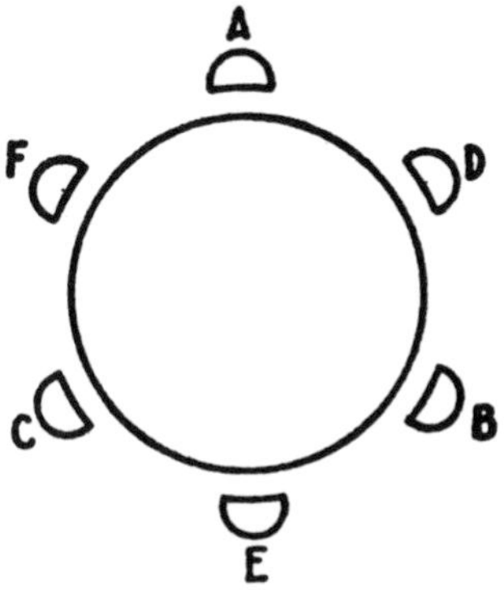

The wife of the engineer must be Mrs Joe Fox, because she is the only married woman in the company.

Elizabeth Anderson is not the social worker; neither is she the manager. Valerie Dunn is neither the secretary nor the manager. She is not the nurse, either, because opposite her Susan Evans sits. Elizabeth Anderson sits opposite the manager; therefore, she cannot be the secretary. The manager is not Anderson, or Baker, or Dunn, or Fox. Also, Anderson cannot be the lecturer, because the lecturer sits on the left of Anderson, whereas Anderson sits on the left of Fox.

Elizabeth Anderson must be the nurse; therefore, it follows that Susan Evans, who sits opposite the nurse, is the manager of a shop.

Mary Baker cannot be the secretary, because she sits opposite Valerie Dunn; therefore, Sarah Clark must be the secretary.

The lecturer cannot be sitting beside Anderson; therefore, the lecturer must be Mary Baker, and so Valerie Dunn must be the social worker.

The completed table looks like this:

	Manager	*Social worker*	*Secretary*	*Lecturer*	*Nurse*	*Housewife*
A	o	o	o	o	+	o
B	o	o	o	+	o	o
C	o	o	+	o	o	o
D	o	+	o	o	o	o
E	+	o	o	o	o	o
F	o	o	o	o	o	+